10 minutes a day!

Word Ladders
for Fluency

Photocopiable activities to boost reading, vocabulary, spelling and phonics skills

Ages 6–7

Skipping

Read the clues, then write the words.
Start at the bottom and climb to the top.

s h i p — 5	A large boat. **Change the first letter.**
'Let's buy fish and ___s.' **Change the last letter.**	c h i p — 4
c h i n — 3	This is between your mouth and your neck. **Change the first letter.**
...eg bone. **Change the second letter.**	s h i n — 2
s k i n — 1	This covers your entire body. **Change the last letter.**
	skip

Written by Timothy V. Rasinski

Edited by **Herts for Learning**

Published in the UK by Scholastic Education, 2022

Scholastic Distribution Centre, Bosworth Avenue,
Tournament Fields, Warwick, CV34

Scholastic Ireland, 89E Lagan Road, Dublin Industrial Estate,
Glasnevin, Dublin, D11 HP5F

First published in the US by Scholastic Inc, 2011
Text and illustrations © 2005, Timothy V. Rasinski
© 2022, Scholastic

A CIP catalogue record for this book is available from the
British Library.

ISBN 978-0-7023-0934-2

Printed by Bell & Bain Ltd, Glasgow
This product is made of FSC®-certified and other controlled
material.

Paper made from wood grown in sustainable forests and other
controlled sources.

1 2 3 4 5 6 7 8 9   2 3 4 5 6 7 8 9 0 1

Author
Timothy V. Rasinski

Editorial team
Rachel Morgan, Vicki Yates, Tracey Cowell, Julia Roberts

Design team
Ellen Matlach for Boultinghouse & Boultinghouse, Inc,
Justin Hoffmann, Couper Street Type Co.

Illustration
Teresa Anderko

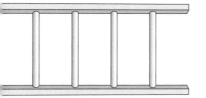
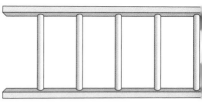

Contents

Foreword 5

How to use 6

Word Ladders

Run, cat, run! 8

Pan-tastic 9

Rats 10

A pat on the back 11

Jam with Sam 12

Wag the tail 13

Everybody clap your hands 14

Camping 15

Jet set 16

Bedtime 17

Word web 18

On the set 19

Make a dent 20

Desk work 21

Ring the bell 22

A big win 23

Put a lid on it 24

Pig fun 25

Sit down 26

Skipping 27

Kiss, kiss 28

Hot, hot, hot 29

Sad story 30

It's a job 31

Dogs 32

Mopping up 33

Stop that! 34

Chop, chop! 35

Socks 36

Fun in the sun 37

Good luck! 38

Don't bug me 39

Rub-a-dub-dub 40

Catch that bus 41

Pump it up 42

Silly squirrel 43

Cluck, cluck 44

Make your bed 45

Number one dad 46

Get a leg up 47

Bug on a log 48

Bat attack 49

Tug of war 50

Top hat 51

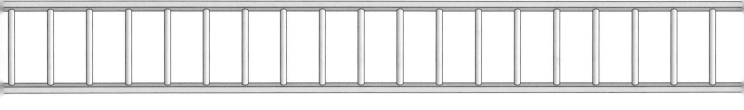

Tap dance............................ 52

Top dog............................... 53

Cup of tea.......................... 54

High tide............................. 55

Give a dog a bone.............. 56

Swimming............................ 57

Shipshape............................ 58

In a rush............................. 59

Make a list.......................... 60

Stack of books.................... 61

Stamp it.............................. 62

Wishing well........................ 63

Cow fun.............................. 64

Sort it out........................... 65

Girl power........................... 66

Pack your bags................... 67

Lunchtime........................... 68

Looking sharp..................... 69

Aww!.................................. 70

Eww!................................... 71

Look what you know............ 72

Moo, cow, moo................... 73

Dig in the soil..................... 74

Ring, ring............................ 75

Sing along.......................... 76

Bring it on!......................... 77

Power up............................. 78

Shadow puppets.................. 79

Colour change..................... 80

A matter of size.................. 81

Sweet sounds...................... 82

Hop to it............................. 83

Warm and cosy................... 84

Glasses............................... 85

Top to bottom..................... 86

Different ways to travel....... 87

Fab fruits........................... 88

Beautiful forests................. 89

Deep sea divers.................. 90

Toy shop............................. 91

Answers **92**

 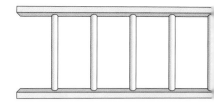

Foreword

In the UK, the first stage of teaching reading focuses on phonics, with an emphasis on children learning to decode the words on the page. The essential skills of language knowledge, fluency and comprehension are developed alongside.

The National Curriculum states: 'Good comprehension draws from linguistic knowledge (in particular of vocabulary and grammar) and on knowledge of the world.' and that 'Skilled word reading involves both the speedy working out of the pronunciation of unfamiliar printed words (decoding) and the speedy recognition of familiar printed words.'

A breadth of vocabulary is a key component to successful reading comprehension. Much research has shown that the breadth of children's vocabulary has a direct correlation with children's reading comprehension and future life chances. In 2002, Beck, McKeown & Kucan, identified a lack of targeted vocabulary instruction in schools, although, nowadays, most UK schools have a vocabulary development approach woven throughout their curriculum. *Daily Word Ladders for Fluency* will provide schools with an invaluable resource to supplement their approach to developing vocabulary breadth, whilst also reinforcing and embedding decoding skills.

Regular use of these word ladders as part of a rich and varied language development programme can support children to become familiar with a wider range of words and their definitions. They can also reinforce spelling patterns and exceptions that the children are learning. Furthermore, as children read the words from these ladders in context they are supported to read with automaticity (rapid word reading without conscious decoding). This allows

them to read with prosody (expressive, phrased reading) which in turn supports comprehension. Through this fluent reading, the children's knowledge of literary language grows.

Developing a playfulness with words is a further benefit of word ladders. Word problems can encourage an excitement around language and may help train concentration. This, in turn, can encourage further interaction and longer periods of concentration. It is well known that succeeding in solving tricky problems helps to develop confidence and boost self-esteem. Success may then lead to increased acceptance of challenges in other areas of learning. Development of vocabulary also supports an increasing knowledge and understanding of the world. In addition, if children work collaboratively on these ladders, they can be taught to build social and oracy skills and learn to take turns when listening to one another. Aside from practical considerations, vocabulary development can also allow children to appreciate the beauty of our language.

Herts for Learning (HfL) recognises the need to support children who can decode but struggle to understand what they read. The *HfL Reading Fluency Project* was founded on the question: if a child reads a text with expert prosody, can that lead to better understanding? Automatic word recognition is intrinsic to the success of this programme, as automaticity when reading supports an appropriate reading rate which is a crucial element for comprehension. Regular engagement with meaningful language play, such as through word ladder activities, ensures that vocabulary breadth and automatised decoding are developed hand in hand. As such, HfL recognises the word ladders as a useful tool to achieving the aims as outlined in the National Curriculum.

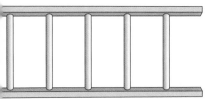

How to use

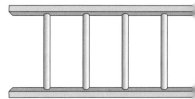

In this book you'll find 84 mini word study lessons that are also child-pleasing games. To complete each word ladder takes just ten minutes but actively involves the learner in analysing the structure and meaning of words. To play, children begin with one word and then make a series of other words by changing or rearranging the letters in the word before. With regular use, word ladders can go a long way towards developing your children's decoding and vocabulary skills.

How do word ladders work?

Let's say our first word ladder begins with the word *web*. The instructions will tell children to change one letter in web to make a word that means 'not dry'. The word children will make is *wet*. The next word will then ask children to make a change in *wet* to form another word – perhaps *pet* or *set*. Children will form new words as they work up the ladder until they reach the top rung. If children get stuck on a rung along the way, they can come back to it because the words before and after will give them the clues they need to figure out the word. Of course, you can also provide additional clues to help them.

How do word ladders benefit children?

Word ladders are great for building children's decoding, phonics, spelling and vocabulary skills. When children add, take away or rearrange letters to make a new word from one they have just made, they must examine sound–symbol relationships closely. This is the kind of analysis that all children need to do in order to learn how to decode and spell accurately. And when the ladder adds meaning in the form of a

definition (for example, 'This blows air to cool you down'), it helps extend children's understanding of words and concepts. All of these skills are key to children's success in learning to read and write. So even though word ladders will feel like a game, children will also be practising essential literacy skills.

How do I teach a word ladder lesson?

Word ladders are incredibly easy and quick to implement. Here are four simple steps:

1. Choose a word ladder to try. (The first thirty or so are easier than the others.)
2. Make a copy for each child.
3. Choose whether you want to do the word ladder with the class as a whole, or for children to work alone, in pairs, or in groups. If children are emergent readers, you could read the clues to them and use a think-aloud method to model how to complete the activity. In addition, you could display the word ladder on the whiteboard to demonstrate how to fill in the word on each rung. As their skills develop, children can begin doing the word ladders independently.
4. For each new word, children will see two clues: the kinds of changes they need to make to the previous word ('Change the first letter', 'Add a letter to the end', and so on), and a definition of or clue to the meaning of the word. Sometimes this clue will be a sentence in which the word is used in context but is left out for children to fill in. Move from word to word in this way, up the whole word ladder. Feel free to add clues if the word is challenging – letter position of the change; other sentence clues; or just tell children the word.

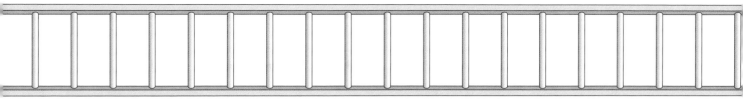

Look for the **bonus boxes** with stars. These are particularly difficult words you may want to pre-teach. Or you can do these ladders as a group so that children will not get stuck on this rung.

That's the lesson in a nutshell! It should take no longer than ten minutes to do. Once you're finished, you may wish to extend the lesson by asking children to sort the words into various categories. This can help them deepen their understanding of word relationships. For instance, they could sort them into:

- grammatical categories (Which words are nouns? Verbs?)

- word structure (Which words have a long vowel and which don't? Which contain a consonant blend?)

- word meaning (Which words express what a person can do or feel? Which do not?)

About the author
Timothey V. Rasinski is professor of literacy education at Kent State University in Ohio. He began his career as a classroom teacher. Since then, he's written and edited more than 50 books and 200 articles on reading education, including the best-selling *Megabook of Fluency* and the seminal *The Fluent Reader*.

In 2020, the International Literacy Association awarded Tim the William S. Gray Citation of Merit honour. This award honours a nationally or internationally known individual for their outstanding contributions to the field of reading/literacy. Of Tim, the International Literacy Association said 'Tim Rasinski is one of those names that's synonymous with high-quality literacy research, resources and professional development, especially when it comes to foundational reading and writing skills and struggling readers.'

Tips for working with word ladders

- List all the 'answers' for the ladder (that is, the words for each rung) in random order on the whiteboard. Ask children to choose words from the list to complete the puzzle.

- Add your own clues to give children extra help as they work through each rung of a ladder. A recent event in your classroom or community could even inspire clues for words.

- If children are stuck on a particular rung, say the word aloud and see if children can spell it correctly by making appropriate changes in the previous word. Elaborate on the meanings of the words as children move their way up the ladder.

- Challenge children to come up with alternative definitions for the same words. Many words, like bat, pet and bill, have multiple meanings.

- Once children complete a ladder, add the words to a word wall. Encourage children to use the words in their speaking and writing.

Name _____

Run, cat, run!

Read the clues, then write the words.
Start at the bottom and climb to the top.

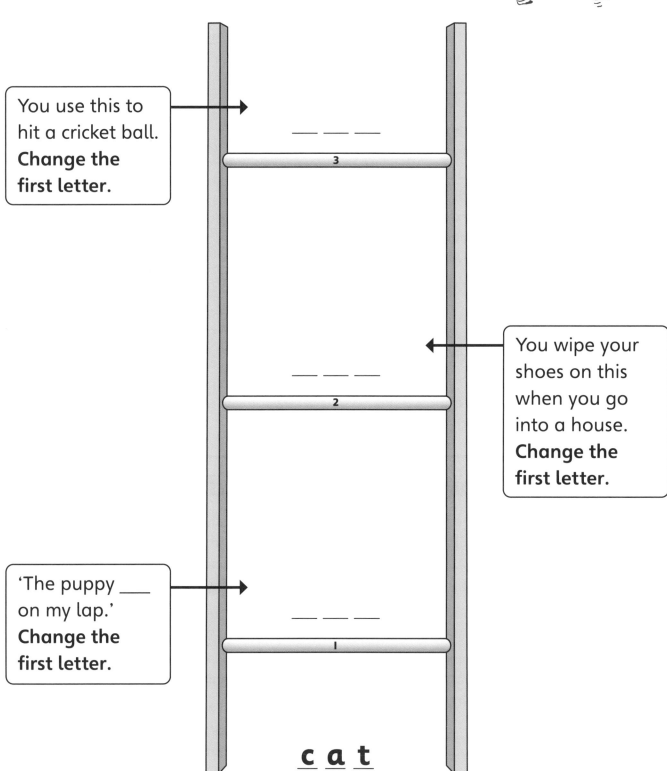

You use this to hit a cricket ball. **Change the first letter.**

→ __ __ __

3

You wipe your shoes on this when you go into a house. **Change the first letter.**

←

__ __ __

2

'The puppy ___ on my lap.' **Change the first letter.**

→

__ __ __

1

<u>c</u> <u>a</u> <u>t</u>

Daily Word Ladders for Fluency **SCHOLASTIC**

Pan-tastic

Read the clues, then write the words.
Start at the bottom and climb to the top.

3   __ __ __

A boy grows up to become a ___.
Change the first letter.

2   __ __ __

This blows air to cool you down.
Change the first letter.

1   __ __ __

'You ___ do this!'
Change the first letter.

p a n

Rats

Read the clues, then write the words.
Start at the bottom and climb to the top.

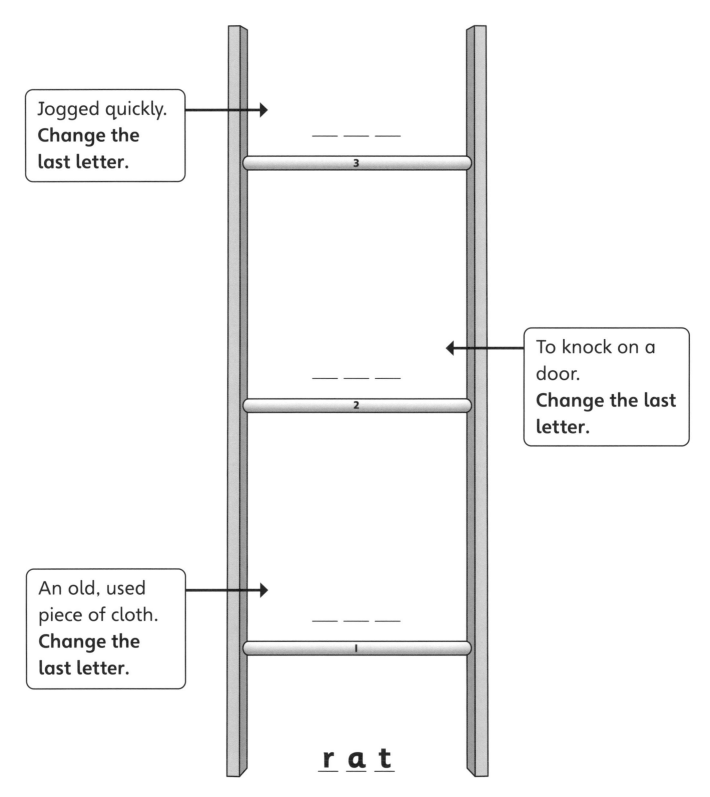

Jogged quickly. **Change the last letter.**

___ ___ ___

3

To knock on a door. **Change the last letter.**

___ ___ ___

2

An old, used piece of cloth. **Change the last letter.**

___ ___ ___

1

r a t

Daily Word Ladders for Fluency **SCHOLASTIC**

Name _____

A pat on the back

Read the clues, then write the words.
Start at the bottom and climb to the top.

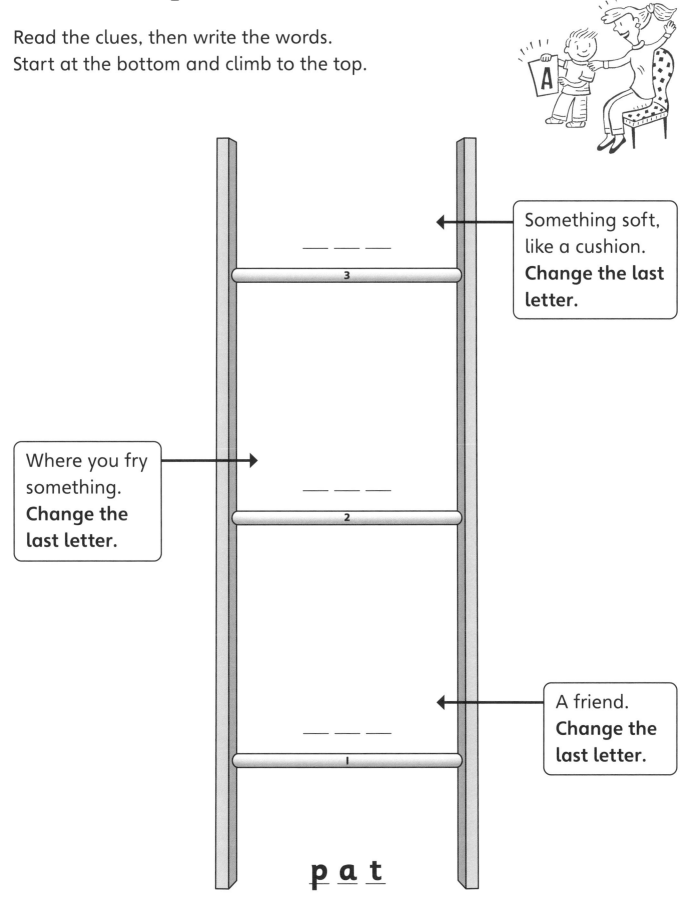

Something soft, like a cushion. **Change the last letter.**

__ __ __   3

Where you fry something. **Change the last letter.**

__ __ __   2

A friend. **Change the last letter.**

__ __ __   1

p a t

Jam with Sam

Read the clues, then write the words.
Start at the bottom and climb to the top.

'She ___ on a chair.'
Change the last letter.

— — —

4

Not *happy*.
Change the last letter.

— — —

3

A boy's name.
Change the first letter.

— — —

2

'She had ___ sandwiches for lunch.'
Change the first letter.

— — —

1

j a m

Name _____

Wag the tail

Read the clues, then write the words.
Start at the bottom and climb to the top.

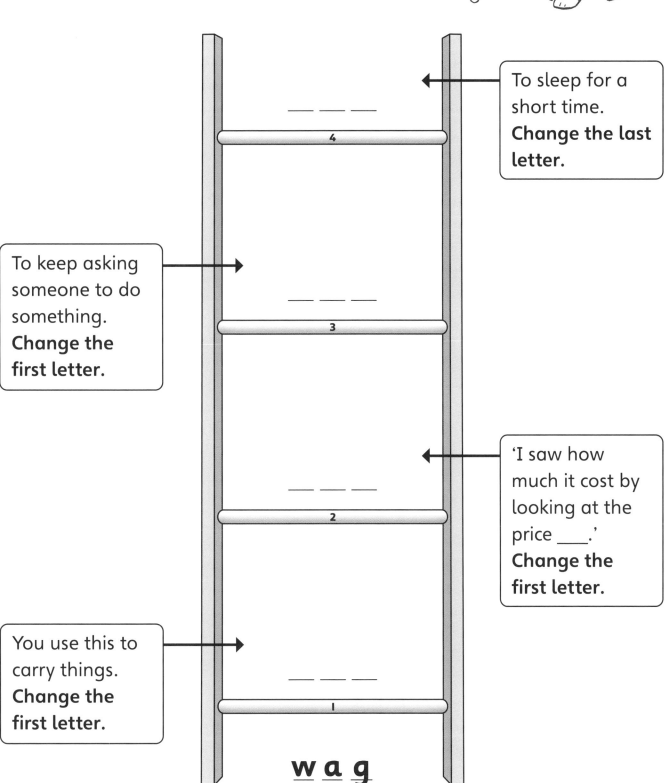

To sleep for a short time. **Change the last letter.**

To keep asking someone to do something. **Change the first letter.**

'I saw how much it cost by looking at the price ___.' **Change the first letter.**

You use this to carry things. **Change the first letter.**

__ __ __ (4)

__ __ __ (3)

__ __ __ (2)

__ __ __ (1)

w a g

Name _____

Everybody clap your hands

Read the clues, then write the words.
Start at the bottom and climb to the top.

'Dad bought a ___ of lemonade.' **Change the last letter.**

___ ___ ___ 5

A taxi. **Change the last letter.**

___ ___ ___ 4

A kind of hat. **Change the first letter.**

___ ___ ___ 3

To touch lightly. **Change the first letter.**

___ ___ ___ 2

'I ran a ___ around the track.' **Take away the first letter.**

___ ___ ___ 1

<u>c</u> <u>l</u> <u>a</u> <u>p</u>

Daily Word Ladders for Fluency **SCHOLASTIC**

Name _____

Camping

Read the clues, then write the words.
Start at the bottom and climb to the top.

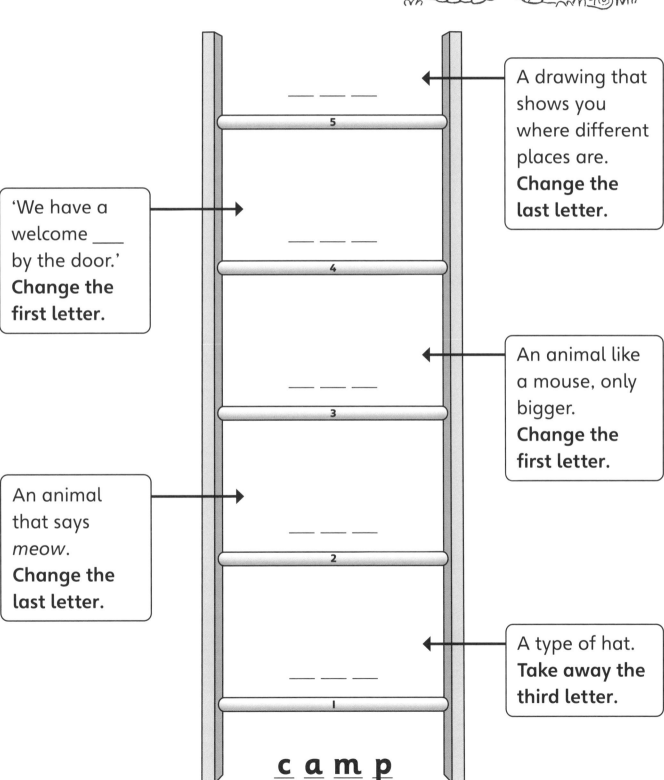

A drawing that shows you where different places are. **Change the last letter.**

'We have a welcome ___ by the door.' **Change the first letter.**

An animal like a mouse, only bigger. **Change the first letter.**

An animal that says *meow*. **Change the last letter.**

A type of hat. **Take away the third letter.**

5 ___ ___ ___

4 ___ ___ ___

3 ___ ___ ___

2 ___ ___ ___

1 ___ ___ ___

<u>c</u> <u>a</u> <u>m</u> <u>p</u>

Name _____

Jet set

Read the clues, then write the words.
Start at the bottom and climb to the top.

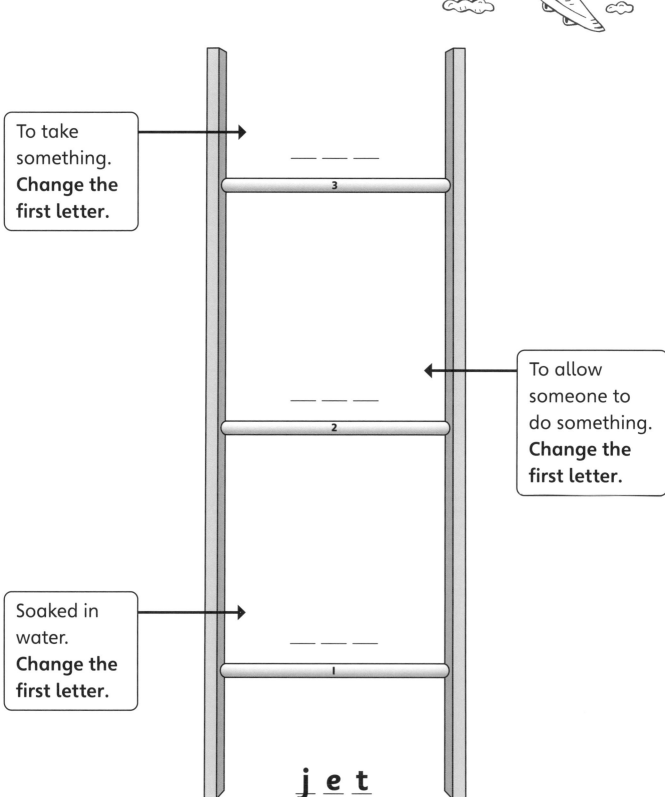

To take something. **Change the first letter.**

__ __ __

3

To allow someone to do something. **Change the first letter.**

__ __ __

2

Soaked in water. **Change the first letter.**

__ __ __

1

j e t

Daily Word Ladders for Fluency ▪SCHOLASTIC

Name _____

Bedtime

Read the clues, then write the words.
Start at the bottom and climb to the top.

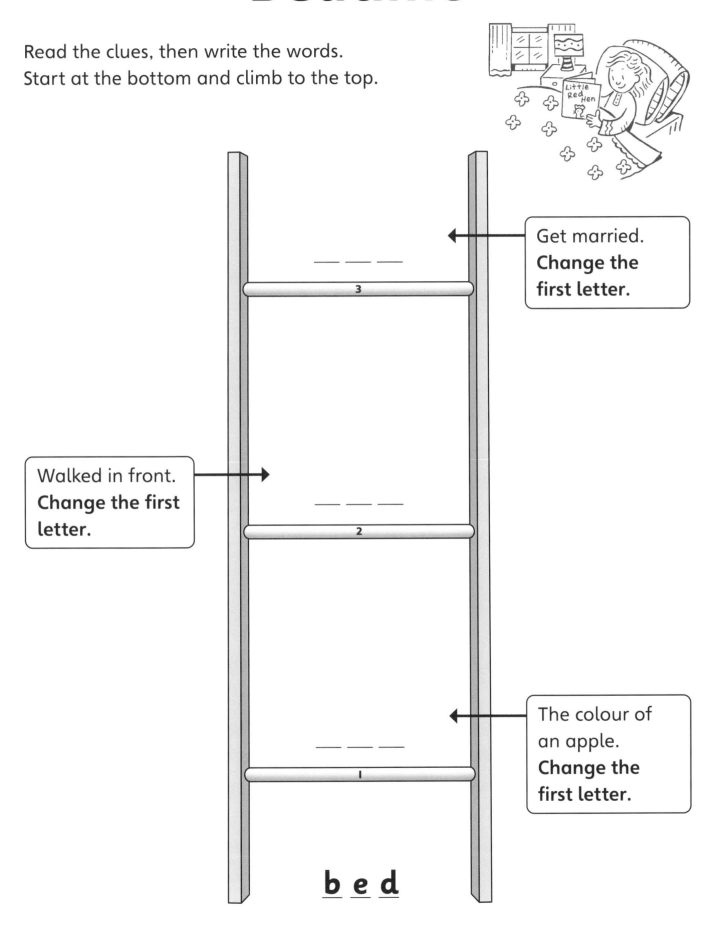

__ __ __

3

Get married.
Change the first letter.

Walked in front.
Change the first letter.

__ __ __

2

__ __ __

1

The colour of an apple.
Change the first letter.

<u>b</u> <u>e</u> <u>d</u>

Name _____

Word web

Read the clues, then write the words.
Start at the bottom and climb to the top.

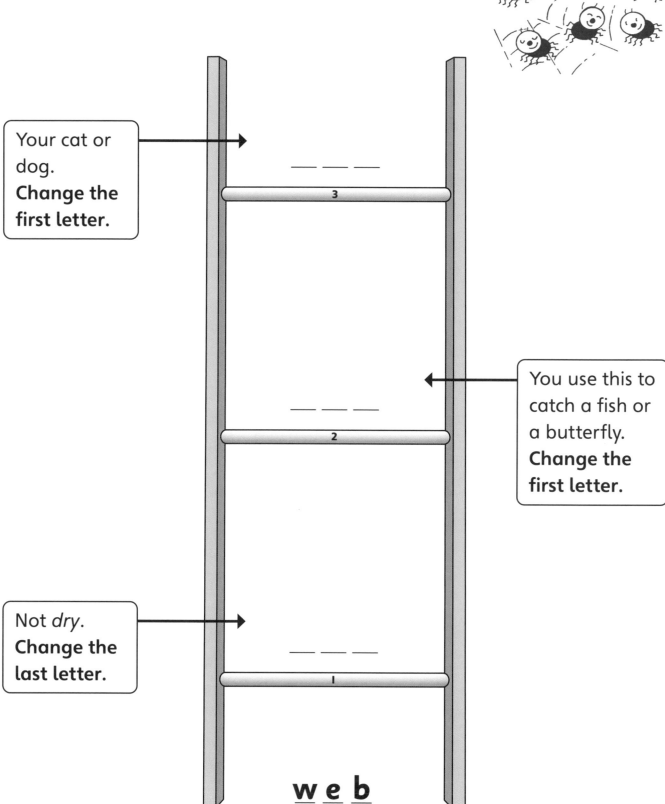

Your cat or dog. **Change the first letter.**

— — —

3

You use this to catch a fish or a butterfly. **Change the first letter.**

— — —

2

Not *dry*. **Change the last letter.**

— — —

1

<u>w</u> <u>e</u> <u>b</u>

Daily Word Ladders for Fluency ■SCHOLASTIC

On the set

Read the clues, then write the words.
Start at the bottom and climb to the top.

__ __ __

4

> Where a bear or fox might sleep. **Change the first letter.**

> Boys grow up to become ___. **Change the last letter.**

__ __ __

3

__ __ __

2

> 'I ___ my friend after school.' **Change the first letter.**

> Opposite of *dry*. **Change the first letter.**

__ __ __

1

<u>s</u> <u>e</u> <u>t</u>

Name _____

Make a dent

Read the clues, then write the words.
Start at the bottom and climb to the top.

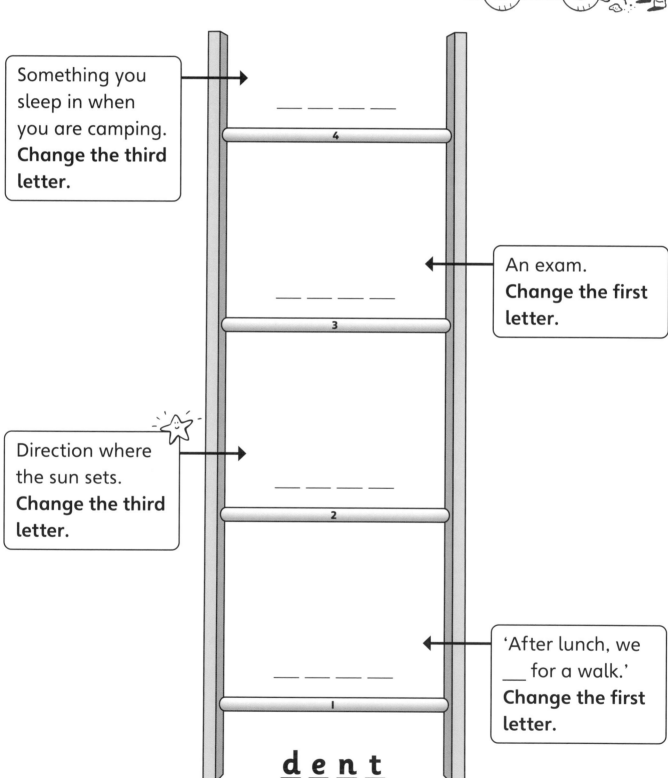

Something you sleep in when you are camping. **Change the third letter.**

— — — — —

4

An exam. **Change the first letter.**

— — — — —

3

Direction where the sun sets. **Change the third letter.**

— — — — —

2

'After lunch, we __ for a walk.' **Change the first letter.**

— — — — —

1

d e n t

Daily Word Ladders for Fluency **SCHOLASTIC**

Name _____

Desk work

Read the clues, then write the words.
Start at the bottom and climb to the top.

Not straight.
Add a letter before the last letter.

To make a guess.
'I ___ he will miss the train.'
Change the first letter.

You might use this to catch a fish.
Take away the last two letters. Add one letter at the end.

A giraffe has a long ___.
Change the first letter.

A pack of cards.
Change the third letter.

5 _ _ _ _ _

4 _ _ _

3 _ _ _

2 _ _ _ _

1 _ _ _ _

<u>d</u> <u>e</u> <u>s</u> <u>k</u>

Name _____

Ring the bell

Read the clues, then write the words.
Start at the bottom and climb to the top.

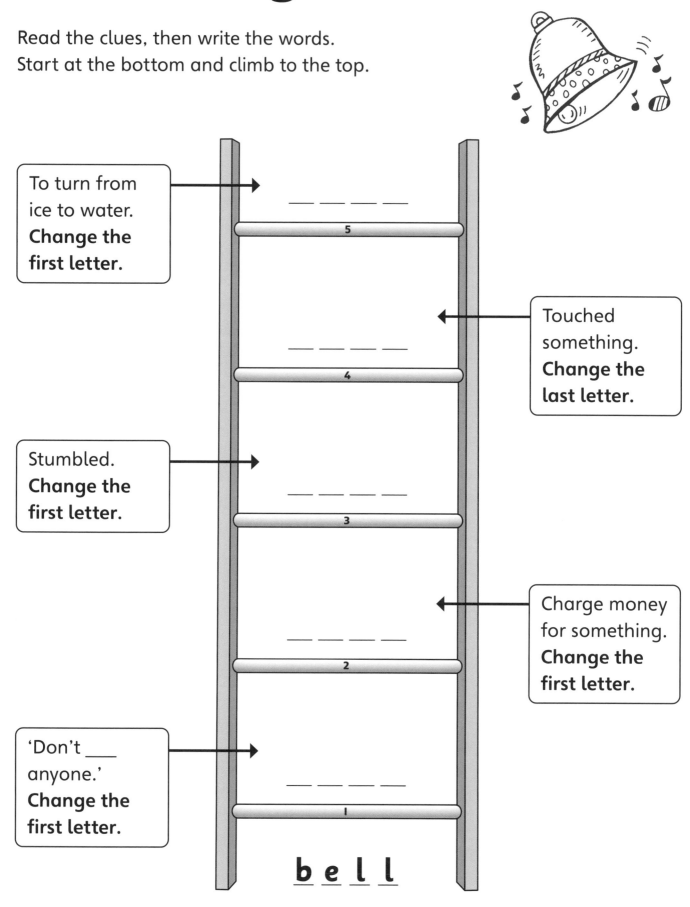

To turn from
ice to water.
**Change the
first letter.**

_ _ _ _ _

5

Touched
something.
**Change the
last letter.**

_ _ _ _

4

Stumbled.
**Change the
first letter.**

_ _ _ _

3

Charge money
for something.
**Change the
first letter.**

_ _ _ _

2

'Don't ___
anyone.'
**Change the
first letter.**

_ _ _ _

1

b e l l

Photocopiable   Daily Word Ladders for Fluency **SCHOLASTIC**

A big win

Read the clues, then write the words.
Start at the bottom and climb to the top.

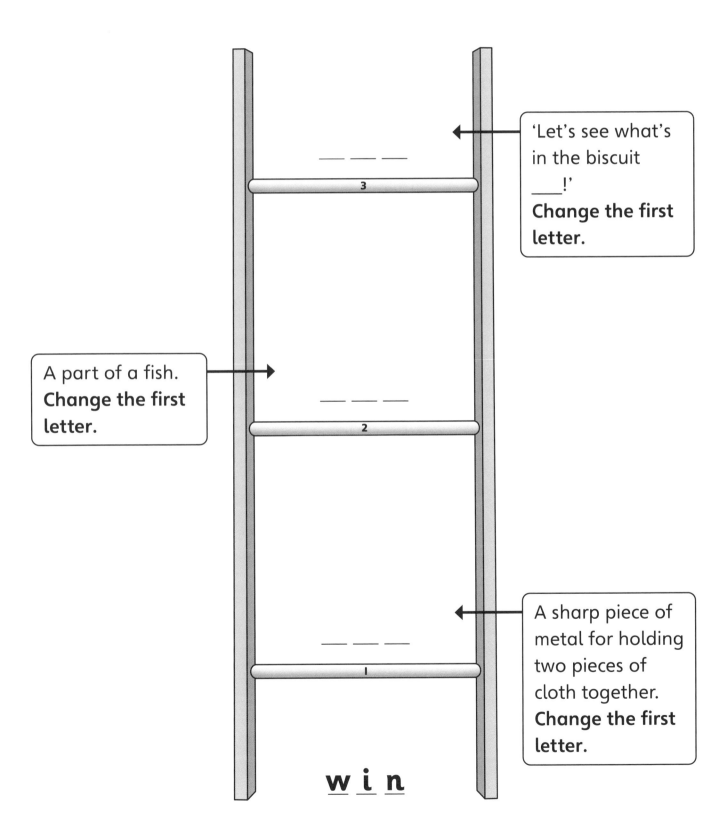

__ __ __
3

'Let's see what's in the biscuit ___!'
Change the first letter.

A part of a fish.
Change the first letter.

__ __ __
2

A sharp piece of metal for holding two pieces of cloth together.
Change the first letter.

__ __ __
1

<u>w</u> <u>i</u> <u>n</u>

Put a lid on it

Read the clues, then write the words.
Start at the bottom and climb to the top.

'What ___ you do yesterday?'
Change the first letter.

___ ___ ___

3

Soap and water get ___ of dirt.
Change the first letter.

___ ___ ___

2

'Mum ___ our presents in the wardrobe.'
Change the first letter.

___ ___ ___

1

<u>l</u> <u>i</u> <u>d</u>

Name _____

Pig fun

Read the clues, then write the words.
Start at the bottom and climb to the top.

Opposite of *lose*.
Change the first letter.

'Farrah put the rubbish in the ___.'
Change the last letter.

A small amount.
Change the last letter.

Large.
Change the first letter.

__ __ __   4

__ __ __   3

__ __ __   2

__ __ __   1

p i g

Sit down

Read the clues, then write the words.
Start at the bottom and climb to the top.

A large boat.
Change the last letter.

→ _ _ _ _ _

4

Bone between your ankle and knee.
Change the second letter.

_ _ _ _ _

3

Turn around and around.
Change the last letter.

→ _ _ _ _ _

2

'After you brush your teeth, ___ out the toothpaste.'
Add a letter after the first letter.

_ _ _ _ _

1

<u>s</u> <u>i</u> <u>t</u>

Daily Word Ladders for Fluency **SCHOLASTIC**

Skipping

Read the clues, then write the words.
Start at the bottom and climb to the top.

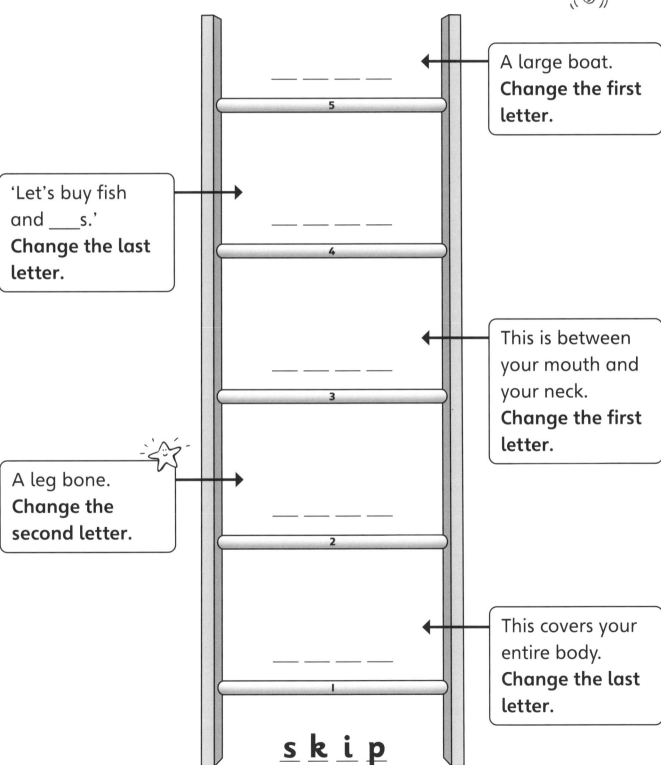

A large boat.
Change the first letter.

'Let's buy fish and ___s.'
Change the last letter.

This is between your mouth and your neck.
Change the first letter.

A leg bone.
Change the second letter.

This covers your entire body.
Change the last letter.

5

4

3

2

1

s k i p

Name _____

Kiss, kiss

Read the clues, then write the words.
Start at the bottom and climb to the top.

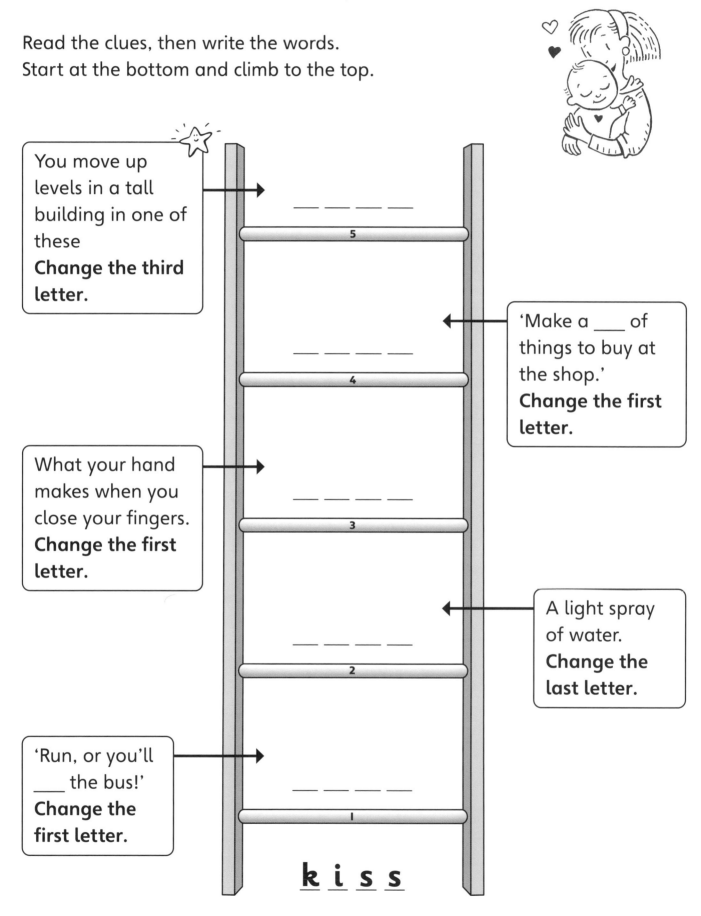

You move up levels in a tall building in one of these
Change the third letter.

_ _ _ _ _

5

'Make a ___ of things to buy at the shop.'
Change the first letter.

_ _ _ _ _

4

What your hand makes when you close your fingers.
Change the first letter.

_ _ _ _ _

3

A light spray of water.
Change the last letter.

_ _ _ _ _

2

'Run, or you'll ___ the bus!'
Change the first letter.

_ _ _ _ _

1

k i s s

Daily Word Ladders for Fluency ■SCHOLASTIC

Name _____

Hot, hot, hot

Read the clues, then write the words.
Start at the bottom and climb to the top.

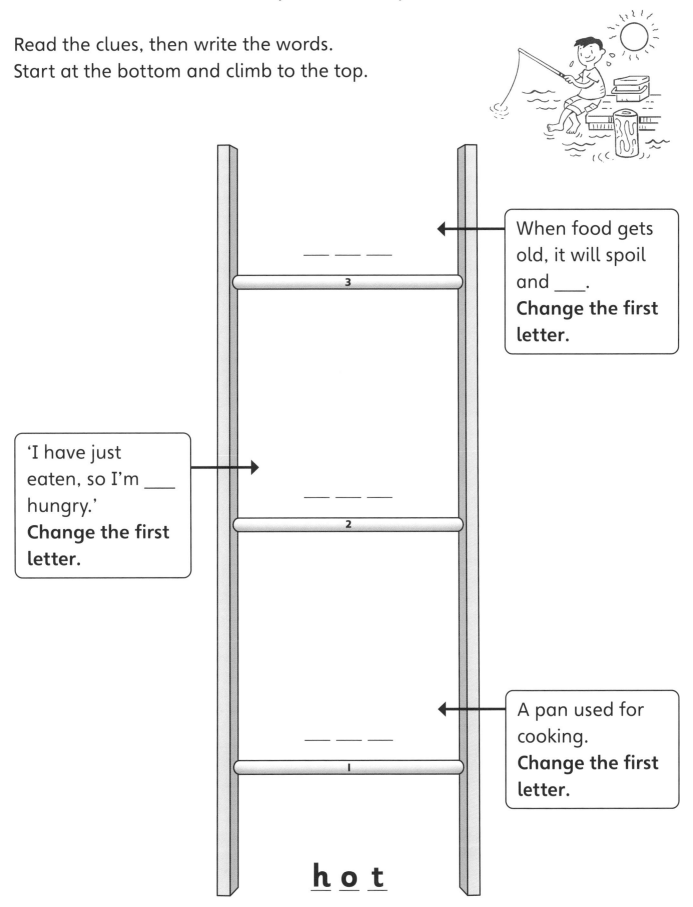

3 — — —

When food gets old, it will spoil and ___.
Change the first letter.

2 — — —

'I have just eaten, so I'm ___ hungry.'
Change the first letter.

1 — — —

A pan used for cooking.
Change the first letter.

h o t

Name _____

Sad story

Read the clues, then write the words.
Start at the bottom and climb to the top.

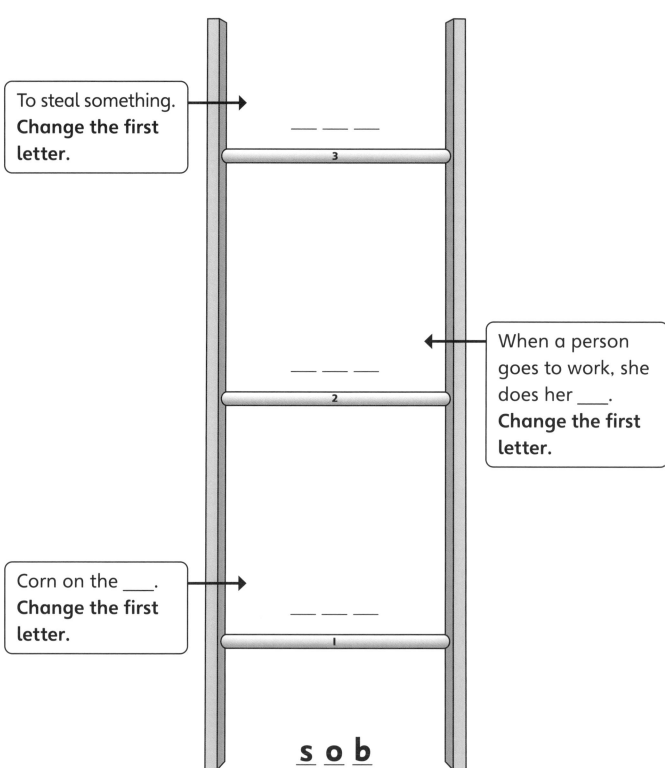

To steal something.
Change the first letter.

— — —

3

When a person goes to work, she does her ___.
Change the first letter.

— — —

2

Corn on the ___.
Change the first letter.

— — —

1

<u>s</u> <u>o</u> <u>b</u>

Daily Word Ladders for Fluency **SCHOLASTIC**

Name _____

It's a job

Read the clues, then write the words.
Start at the bottom and climb to the top.

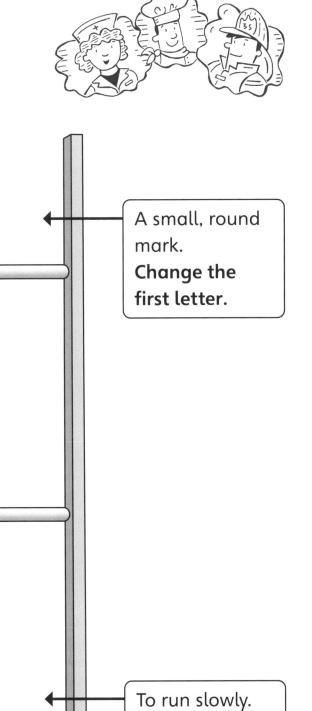

_ _ _
3

A small, round mark. **Change the first letter.**

To write something quickly. **Change the last letter.**

_ _ _
2

To run slowly. **Change the last letter.**

_ _ _
1

j o b

Name _____

Dogs

Read the clues, then write the words.
Start at the bottom and climb to the top.

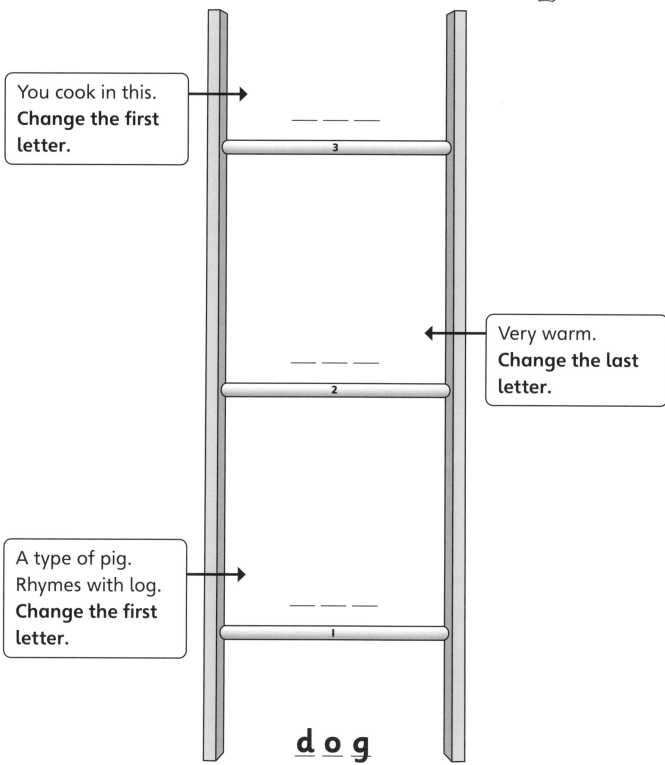

You cook in this.
Change the first letter.

— — —

3

Very warm.
Change the last letter.

— — —

2

A type of pig.
Rhymes with log.
Change the first letter.

— — —

1

<u>d</u> <u>o</u> <u>g</u>

  Daily Word Ladders for Fluency **SCHOLASTIC**

Mopping up

Read the clues, then write the words.
Start at the bottom and climb to the top.

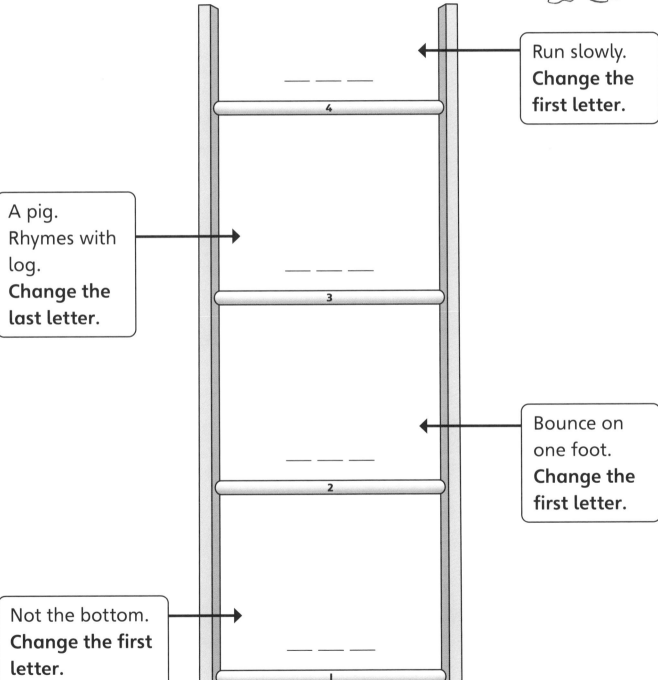

Run slowly. **Change the first letter.**

A pig. Rhymes with log. **Change the last letter.**

Bounce on one foot. **Change the first letter.**

Not the bottom. **Change the first letter.**

4

3

2

1

m o p

Name _____

Stop that!

Read the clues, then write the words.
Start at the bottom and climb to the top.

A bed for a baby. **Change the first letter.** → ___ ___ ___

4

Opposite of *cold*. **Change the last letter.** ← ___ ___ ___

3

A short jump. **Take away the first letter.** → ___ ___ ___

2

A place where you buy things. **Change the second letter.** ← ___ ___ ___ ___

1

<u>s</u> <u>t</u> <u>o</u> <u>p</u>

Photocopiable

Daily Word Ladders for Fluency **SCHOLASTIC**

Name _____

Chop, chop!

Read the clues, then write the words.
Start at the bottom and climb to the top.

You open this with a key. **Take away the last letter. Add two letters at the end.**

5 ___ ___ ___ ___

The opposite of *a little* is a ___. **Change the first letter.**

4 ___ ___ ___

Very warm. **Take away the first letter.**

3 ___ ___ ___

'The football player took a ___.' **Change the last letter.**

2 ___ ___ ___ ___

A place where you buy things. **Change the first letter.**

1 ___ ___ ___ ___

<u>c</u> <u>h</u> <u>o</u> <u>p</u>

Socks

Read the clues, then write the words.
Start at the bottom and climb to the top.

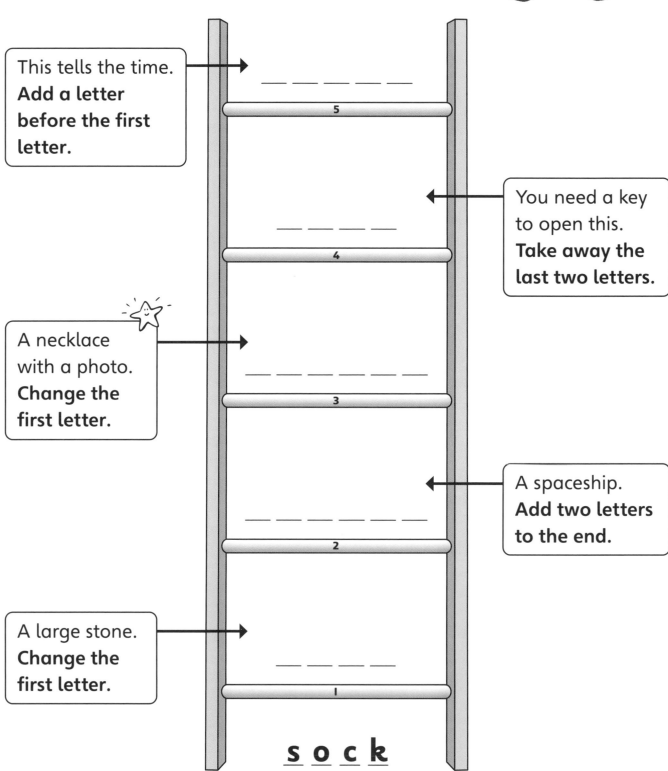

This tells the time. **Add a letter before the first letter.**

5 _ _ _ _ _ _

You need a key to open this. **Take away the last two letters.**

4 _ _ _ _ _

A necklace with a photo. **Change the first letter.**

3 _ _ _ _ _ _ _

A spaceship. **Add two letters to the end.**

2 _ _ _ _ _ _

A large stone. **Change the first letter.**

1 _ _ _ _ _

<u>s o c k</u>

Daily Word Ladders for Fluency ■SCHOLASTIC

Name _____

Fun in the sun

Read the clues, then write the words.
Start at the bottom and climb to the top.

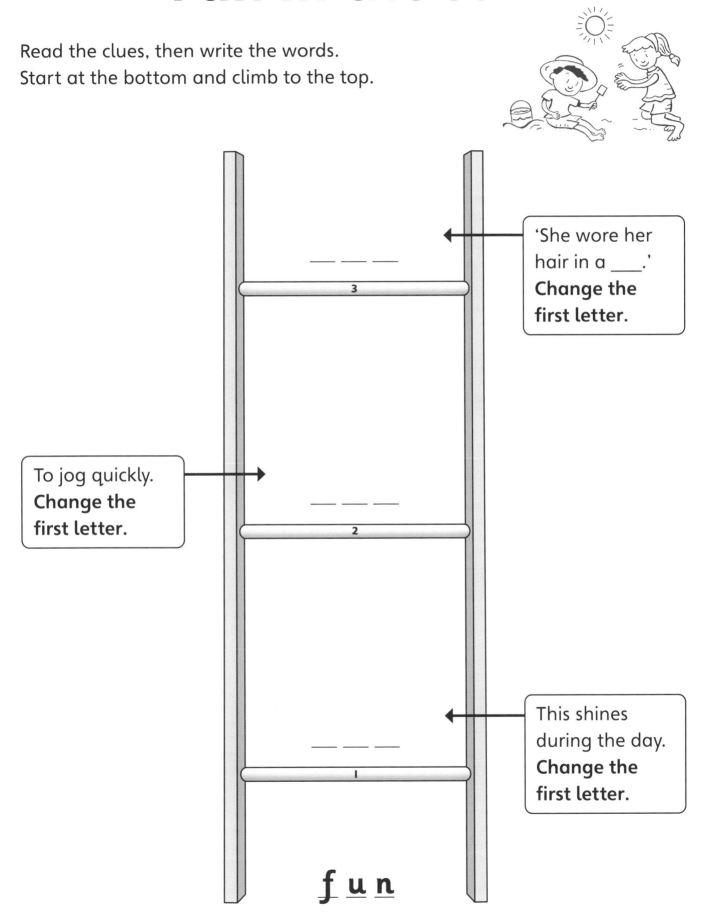

'She wore her hair in a ___.'
Change the first letter.

3 — — —

To jog quickly.
Change the first letter.

2 — — —

This shines during the day.
Change the first letter.

1 — — —

f u n

Good luck!

Read the clues, then write the words.
Start at the bottom and climb to the top.

'The door is ____!
Please help me
open it.'
**Add a letter
before the first
letter.**

_ _ _ _ _ _

3

'Mum, can you
__ me into bed?'
**Change the first
letter.**

_ _ _ _ _

2

A bird that says
quack.
**Change the first
letter.**

_ _ _ _ _

1

<u>l u c k</u>

Name _____

Don't bug me

Read the clues, then write the words.
Start at the bottom and climb to the top.

A young flower.
Change the last letter.

3 ___ ___ ___

A hairstyle that a ballerina usually wears.
Change the last letter.

2 ___ ___ ___

'I take the ___ to school.'
Change the last letter.

1 ___ ___ ___

<u>b u g</u>

Name _____

Rub-a-dub-dub

Read the clues, then write the words.
Start at the bottom and climb to the top.

A step on a ladder.
Add a letter to the end.

3 _ _ _ _ _

To jog very fast.
Change the last letter.

2 _ _ _

A small carpet.
Change the last letter.

1

<u>r</u> <u>u</u> <u>b</u>

Catch that bus

Read the clues, then write the words.
Start at the bottom and climb to the top.

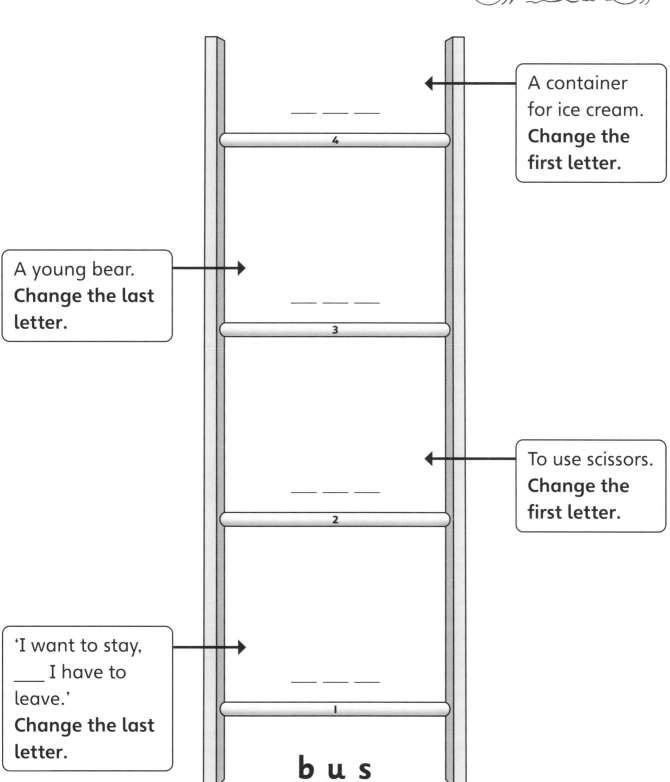

A container for ice cream. **Change the first letter.**

A young bear. **Change the last letter.**

To use scissors. **Change the first letter.**

'I want to stay, ___ I have to leave.' **Change the last letter.**

__ __ __   4

__ __ __   3

__ __ __   2

__ __ __   1

<u>b</u> <u>u</u> <u>s</u>

Pump it up

Read the clues, then write the words.
Start at the bottom and climb to the top.

A large lump on
a camel's back.
**Change the first
letter.**

→ _ _ _ _
4

← To knock into
something.
**Take away the
first two letters.
Add one letter at
the beginning.**

_ _ _ _
3

Soft and round.
**Add a letter at
the beginning.**

→ _ _ _ _ _
2

← When you hit your
head, sometimes
a ___ forms.
**Change the first
letter.**

_ _ _ _
1

p u m p

Name _____

Silly squirrel

Read the clues, then write the words.
Start at the bottom and climb to the top.

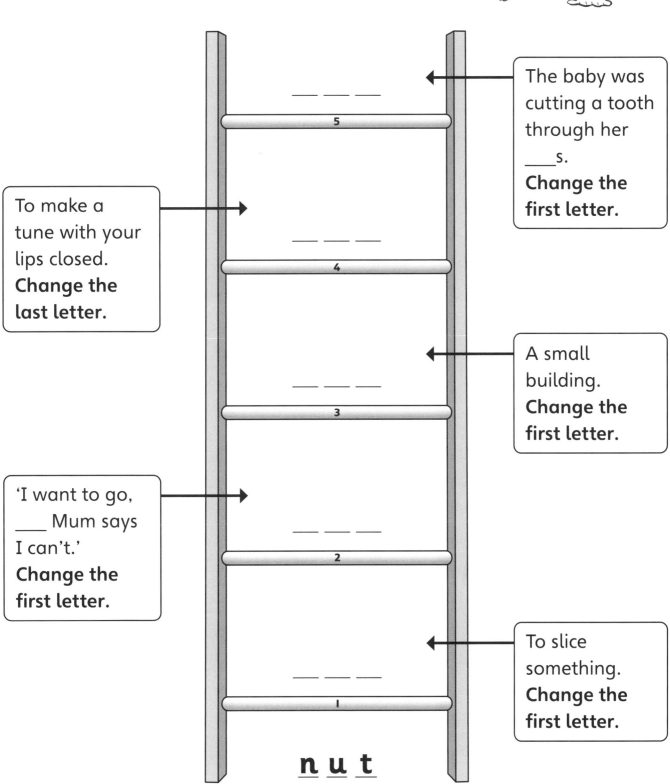

The baby was cutting a tooth through her ___s.
Change the first letter.

To make a tune with your lips closed.
Change the last letter.

A small building.
Change the first letter.

'I want to go, ___ Mum says I can't.'
Change the first letter.

To slice something.
Change the first letter.

5 _ _ _

4 _ _ _

3 _ _ _

2 _ _ _

1 _ _ _

n u t

Cluck, cluck

Read the clues, then write the words.
Start at the bottom and climb to the top.

A large vehicle. **Add a letter after the first letter.**

→ _ _ _ _ _ _

5

‘I hope Mum will ___ me into bed tonight.’ **Change the first letter.** ←

_ _ _ _

4

‘That smells awful. ___!’ **Change the first letter.** →

_ _ _ _

3

A bird that says quack. **Change the first letter.** ←

_ _ _ _

2

‘Good ___ in the match!’ **Take away the first letter.** →

_ _ _ _

1

<u>c l u c k</u>

Name _____

Make your bed

Read the clues, then write the words.
Start at the bottom and climb to the top.

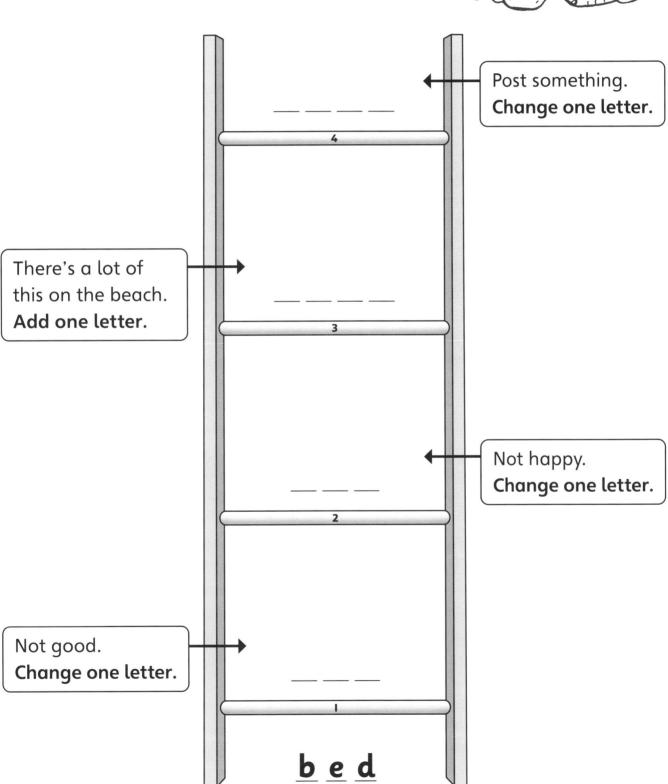

Post something.
Change one letter.

_ _ _ _

4

There's a lot of this on the beach.
Add one letter.

_ _ _ _

3

Not happy.
Change one letter.

_ _ _

2

Not good.
Change one letter.

_ _ _

1

b e d

Name _____

Number one dad

Read the clues, then write the words.
Start at the bottom and climb to the top.

An animal that flies at night. **Change one letter.**

→ __ __ __

5

Not good. **Change one letter.**

__ __ __

4

'We __ pizza for lunch.' **Change one letter.**

→ __ __ __

3

'The dog ___ under the bed because it was afraid.' **Change one letter.**

__ __ __

2

'After school, I __ my homework.' **Change the middle letter.**

→ __ __ __

1

<u>d</u> <u>a</u> <u>d</u>

Daily Word Ladders for Fluency **SCHOLASTIC**

Name _____

Get a leg up

Read the clues, then write the words.
Start at the bottom and climb to the top.

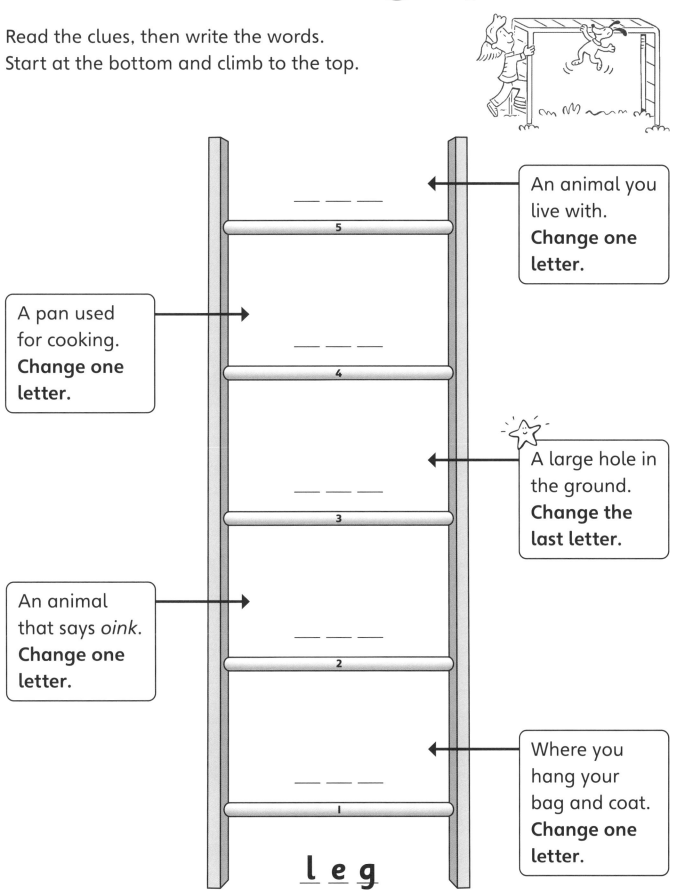

An animal you live with. **Change one letter.**

A pan used for cooking. **Change one letter.**

A large hole in the ground. **Change the last letter.**

An animal that says *oink*. **Change one letter.**

Where you hang your bag and coat. **Change one letter.**

5 __ __ __

4 __ __ __

3 __ __ __

2 __ __ __

1 __ __ __

<u>l</u> <u>e</u> <u>g</u>

Bug on a log

Read the clues, then write the words.
Start at the bottom and climb to the top.

To put your arms around someone. **Change one letter.**

__ __ __ 5

Another name for *pig*. Rhymes with log. **Change one letter.**

__ __ __ 4

A puppy grows up to be a ___. **Change one letter.**

__ __ __ 3

To make a hole in the ground. **Change one letter.**

__ __ __ 2

Large. **Change one letter.**

__ __ __ 1

<u>b</u> <u>u</u> <u>g</u>

Name _____

Bat attack

Read the clues, then write the words.
Start at the bottom and climb to the top.

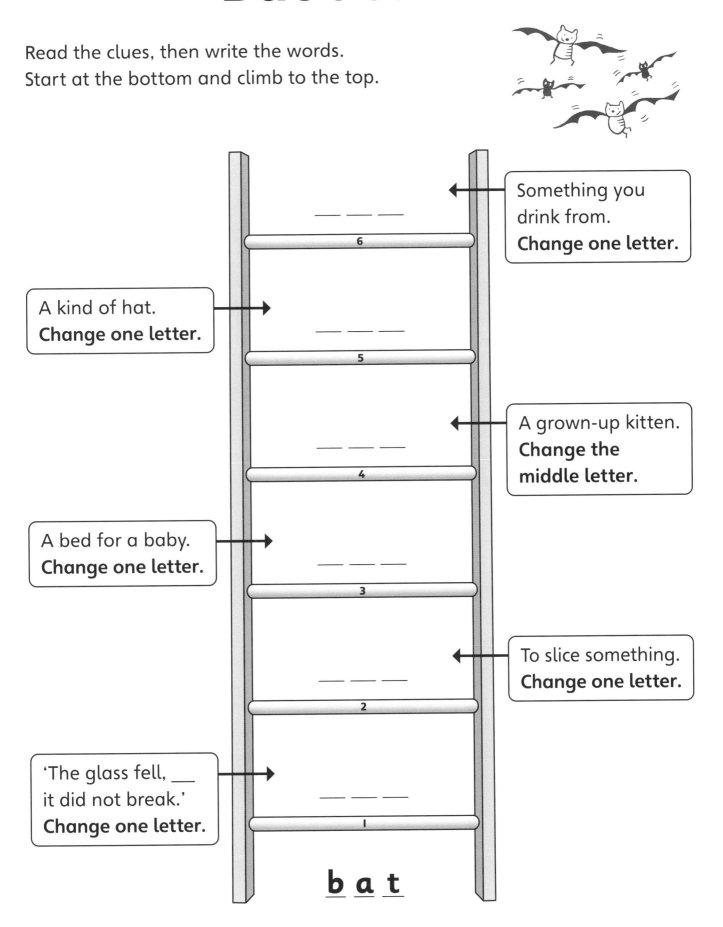

Something you drink from. **Change one letter.**

A kind of hat. **Change one letter.**

A grown-up kitten. **Change the middle letter.**

A bed for a baby. **Change one letter.**

To slice something. **Change one letter.**

'The glass fell, ___ it did not break.' **Change one letter.**

6 ___ ___ ___

5 ___ ___ ___

4 ___ ___ ___

3 ___ ___ ___

2 ___ ___ ___

1 ___ ___ ___

<u>b</u> <u>a</u> <u>t</u>

Name _____

Tug of war

Read the clues, then write the words.
Start at the bottom and climb to the top.

A kind of plane.
Change one letter.

_ _ _
6

To write a quick note.
Change one letter.

_ _ _
5

What someone does for work.
Change the first letter.

_ _ _
4

To steal.
Change one letter.

_ _ _
3

'___-a-dub-dub.'
Change one letter.

_ _ _
2

A covering for the floor.
Change one letter.

_ _ _
1

<u>t u g</u>

Photocopiable

Daily Word Ladders for Fluency **SCHOLASTIC**

Name _____

Top hat

Read the clues, then write the words.
Start at the bottom and climb to the top.

A small, simple building.
Change one letter.

Opposite of *cold*.
Change one letter.

Some flowers grow in a ___.
Change one letter.

A deep hole.
Change the middle letter.

Your cat or dog.
Change one letter.

A light tap on the head or back.
Change one letter.

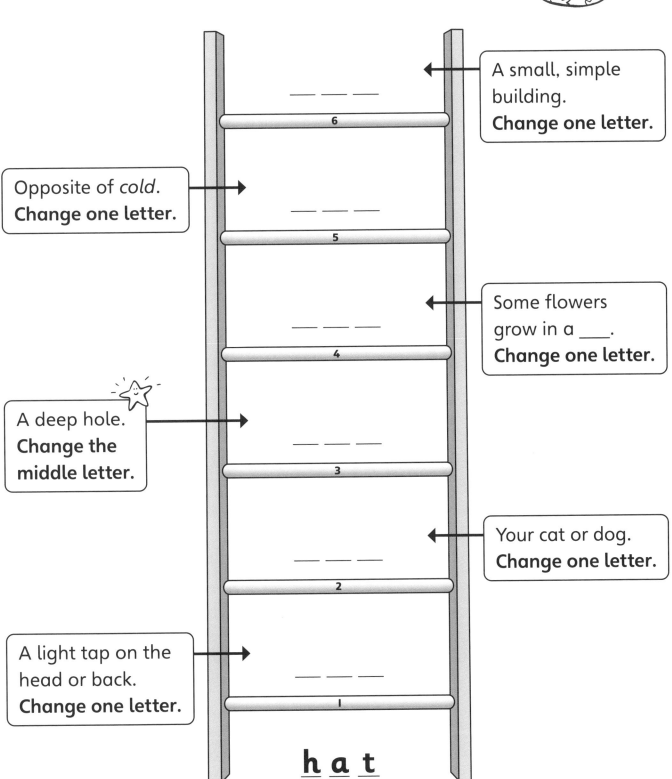

__ __ __   6

__ __ __   5

__ __ __ __   4

__ __ __   3

__ __ __   2

__ __ __   1

h a t

Name _____

Tap dance

Read the clues, then write the words.
Start at the bottom and climb to the top.

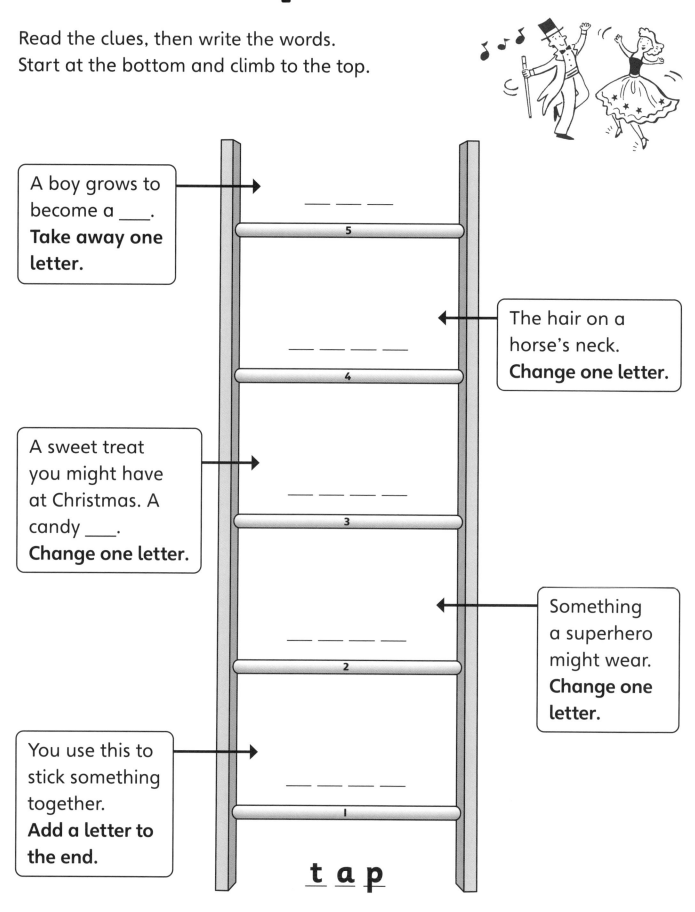

A boy grows to become a ___.
Take away one letter.

_ _ _ _ 5

The hair on a horse's neck.
Change one letter.

_ _ _ _ 4

A sweet treat you might have at Christmas. A candy ___.
Change one letter.

_ _ _ _ 3

Something a superhero might wear.
Change one letter.

_ _ _ _ 2

You use this to stick something together.
Add a letter to the end.

_ _ _ _ 1

t a p

Daily Word Ladders for Fluency **SCHOLASTIC**

Top dog

Read the clues, then write the words.
Start at the bottom and climb to the top.

5. _ _ _ _

You use this to clean the floor. **Take away the last letter.**

To be sad and gloomy. **Change one letter.**

4. _ _ _ _

Thick string. **Change one letter.**

3. _ _ _ _ _

To wish for something. **Add a letter to the end.**

2. _ _ _ _

To jump like a bunny. **Change one letter.**

1. _ _ _

t o p

Name _____

Cup of tea

Read the clues, then write the words.
Start at the bottom and climb to the top.

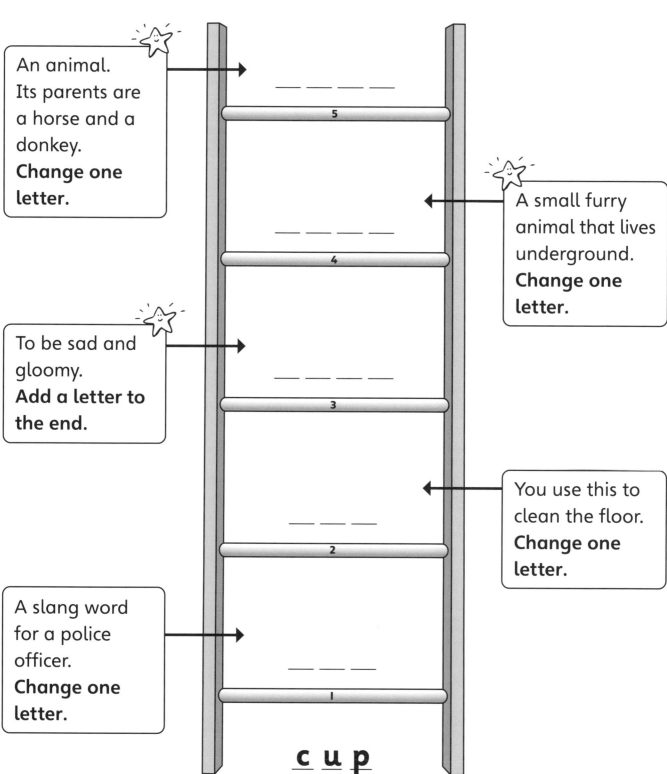

An animal.
Its parents are
a horse and a
donkey.
**Change one
letter.**

A small furry
animal that lives
underground.
**Change one
letter.**

To be sad and
gloomy.
**Add a letter to
the end.**

You use this to
clean the floor.
**Change one
letter.**

A slang word
for a police
officer.
**Change one
letter.**

5

4

3

2

1

c u p

Daily Word Ladders for Fluency ■ SCHOLASTIC

Name _____

High tide

Read the clues, then write the words.
Start at the bottom and climb to the top.

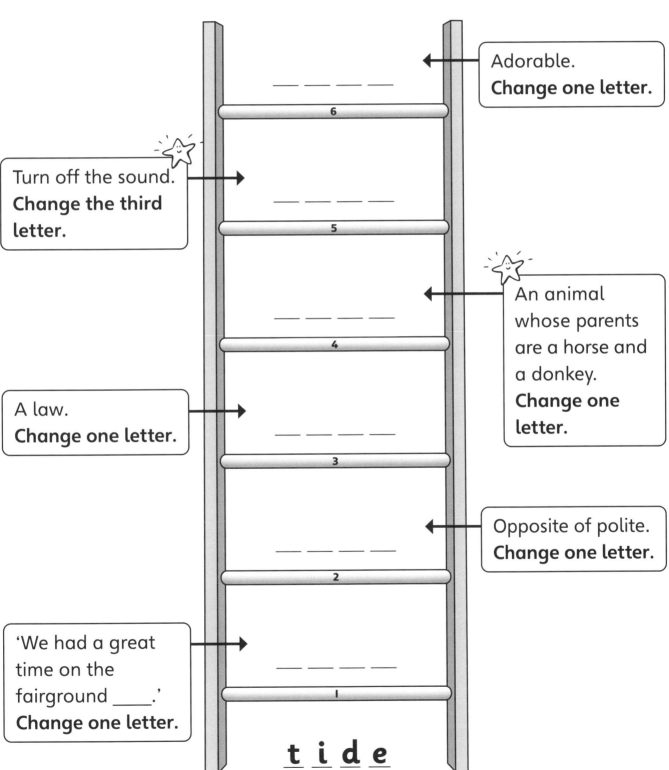

Adorable.
Change one letter.

— — — — —
6

Turn off the sound.
Change the third letter.

— — — —
5

An animal whose parents are a horse and a donkey.
Change one letter.

— — — —
4

A law.
Change one letter.

— — — — —
3

Opposite of polite.
Change one letter.

— — — — —
2

'We had a great time on the fairground ____.'
Change one letter.

— — — — —
1

t i d e

Give a dog a bone

Read the clues, then write the words.
Start at the bottom and climb to the top.

Opposite of early.
Change one letter.

— — — — — 6

A small body of water.
Change one letter.

— — — — 5

To create.
Change one letter.

— — — — 4

Hair on a horse's neck.
Change one letter.

— — — — 3

A sweet treat you might eat at Christmas. A candy ____.
Change one letter.

— — — — 2

Ice cream comes in this.
Change one letter.

— — — — 1

<u>b</u> <u>o</u> <u>n</u> <u>e</u>

Swimming

Read the clues, then write the words.
Start at the bottom and climb to the top.

5 _ _ _ _ _ _

A tool for holding two pieces of wood together. **Add one letter to the end.**

An ocean animal that has a top and bottom shell. **Change one letter.**

4 _ _ _ _

To shut a door loudly. **Change one letter.**

3 _ _ _ _ _

Thin. **Change the second letter.**

2 _ _ _ _

If you read through something quickly, you ___ it. **Change one letter.**

1 _ _ _ _

<u>s</u> <u>w</u> <u>i</u> <u>m</u>

Shipshape

Read the clues, then write the words.
Start at the bottom and climb to the top.

Something to cover your head. **Change one letter.**

__ __ __

5

A small house. **Take away one letter.**

__ __ __

4

Closed the door. **Change one letter.**

__ __ __ __

3

'That kick was amazing. What a great ___!' **Change one letter.**

__ __ __ __

2

A place where you buy things. **Change one letter.**

__ __ __ __

1

s h i p

Daily Word Ladders for Fluency **SCHOLASTIC**

Name _____

In a rush

Read the clues, then write the words.
Start at the bottom and climb to the top.

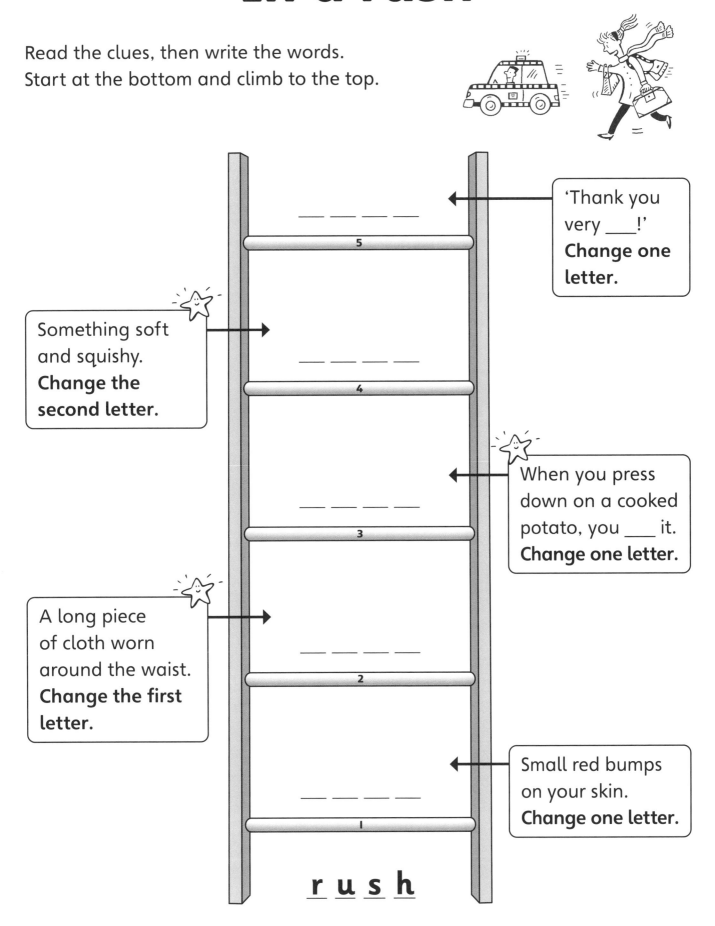

_ _ _ _ _ (5)

'Thank you very ___!' **Change one letter.**

Something soft and squishy. **Change the second letter.**

_ _ _ _ _ (4)

_ _ _ _ (3)

When you press down on a cooked potato, you ___ it. **Change one letter.**

A long piece of cloth worn around the waist. **Change the first letter.**

_ _ _ _ (2)

Small red bumps on your skin. **Change one letter.**

_ _ _ _ (1)

r u s h

Make a list

Read the clues, then write the words.
Start at the bottom and climb to the top.

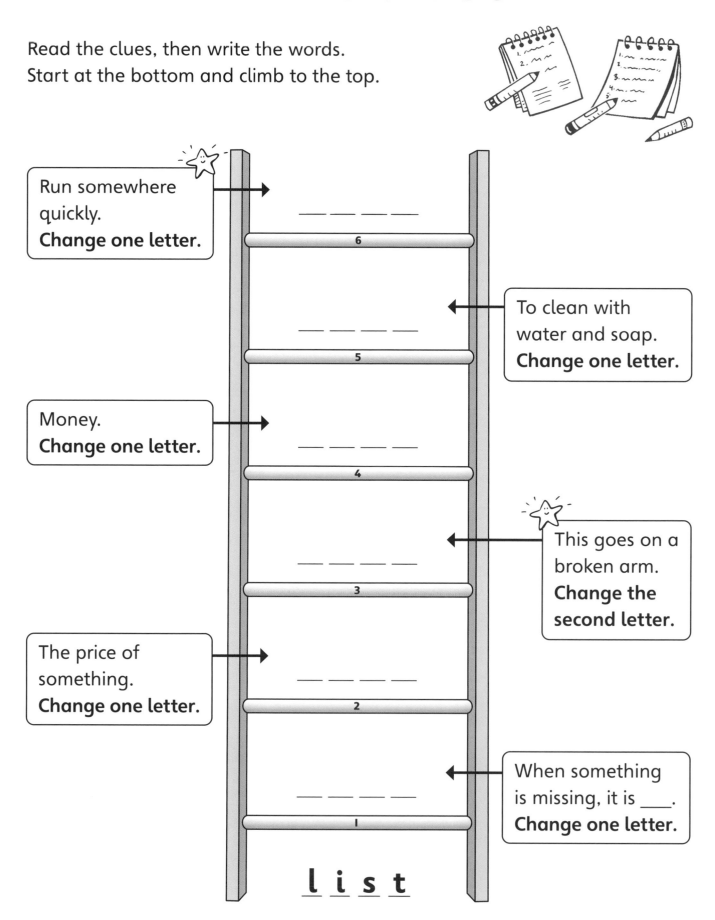

Run somewhere quickly.
Change one letter.

6 _ _ _ _ _

To clean with water and soap.
Change one letter.

5 _ _ _ _

Money.
Change one letter.

4 _ _ _ _

This goes on a broken arm.
Change the second letter.

3 _ _ _ _

The price of something.
Change one letter.

2 _ _ _ _

When something is missing, it is ___.
Change one letter.

1 _ _ _ _

l i s t

Stack of books

Read the clues, then write the words.
Start at the bottom and climb to the top.

6 — _ _ _ _

To cut with an axe.
Change one letter.

A place where you buy things.
Change one letter.

5 — _ _ _ _

A large boat.
Change one letter.

4 — _ _ _ _

To make a small cut with scissors.
Change one letter.

3 — _ _ _ _

To break with a loud, cracking sound.
Take away the last two letters. Add a letter at the end.

2 — _ _ _ _

A bit of food between meals.
Change the second letter.

1 — _ _ _ _ _

s t a c k

Stamp it

Read the clues, then write the words.
Start at the bottom and climb to the top.

A side of a room.
Change one letter.

_ _ _ _ _

6

To take a stroll.
**Take away the
first two letters.
Add one letter to
the beginning.**

_ _ _ _ _

5

A white or
coloured stick. You
use it for writing
and drawing.
**Take away the
first letter. Add
two letters to the
beginning.**

_ _ _ _ _

4

To chat.
Change one letter.

_ _ _ _

3

The equipment
that a horse
needs.
**Take away the
first letter.**

_ _ _ _

2

To put in a pile.
**Change the last
two letters.**

_ _ _ _ _

1

s t a m p

Name _____

Wishing well

Read the clues, then write the words.
Start at the bottom and climb to the top.

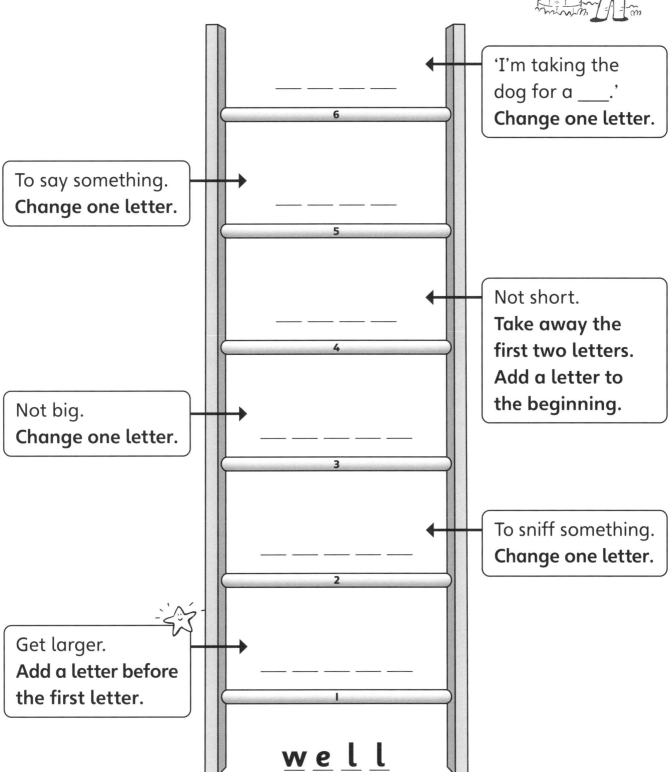

'I'm taking the dog for a ___.'
Change one letter.

To say something.
Change one letter.

Not short.
Take away the first two letters. Add a letter to the beginning.

Not big.
Change one letter.

To sniff something.
Change one letter.

Get larger.
Add a letter before the first letter.

6

5

4

3

2

1

w e l l

Name _____

Cow fun

Read the clues, then write the words.
Start at the bottom and climb to the top.

'Do not run,
just ___.'
**Change one
letter.**

→ __ __ __ __

5

The sides of
a room.
**Change one
letter.** ←

__ __ __ __

4

"I ___ eat later."
**Change the last
letter.** →

__ __ __ __

3

Opposite of
tame.
**Change one
letter.** ←

__ __ __ __

2

Gentle, not
harsh.
**Change the
last letter.** →

__ __ __ __

1

<u>m</u> <u>i</u> <u>l</u> <u>k</u>

Daily Word Ladders for Fluency **SCHOLASTIC**

Name _____

Sort it out

Read the clues, then write the words.
Start at the bottom and climb to the top.

5   _ _ _ _ _ ← The centre of an apple. **Take away one letter.**

Number of points in a game. **Change one letter.** → 4   _ _ _ _ _

3   _ _ _ _ _ ← The land next to the ocean. **Change the last letter.**

Not tall. **Change one letter.** → 2   _ _ _ _ _

1   _ _ _ _ _ ← A game like football or hockey. **Add a letter after the first letter.**

<u>s</u> <u>o</u> <u>r</u> t

Name _____

Girl power

Read the clues, then write the words.
Start at the bottom and climb to the top.

A story.
Change one letter.

— — — — —
6

Opposite of short.
Change one letter.

— — — —
5

A round toy.
Change one letter.

— — — — —
4

A large, long room.
Change one letter.

— — — — —
3

A raised area of land.
Change one letter.

— — — — —
2

Part of a fish.
Change one letter.

— — — —
1

g i r l

Daily Word Ladders for Fluency **SCHOLASTIC**

Name _____

Pack your bags

Read the clues, then write the words.
Start at the bottom and climb to the top.

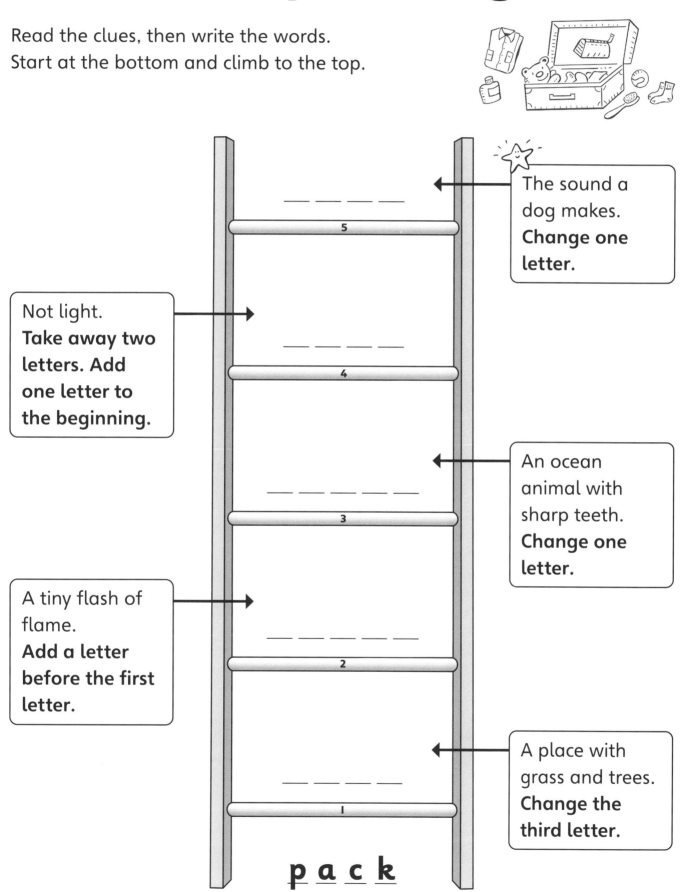

The sound a dog makes. **Change one letter.**

Not light. **Take away two letters. Add one letter to the beginning.**

An ocean animal with sharp teeth. **Change one letter.**

A tiny flash of flame. **Add a letter before the first letter.**

A place with grass and trees. **Change the third letter.**

5 _ _ _ _

4 _ _ _ _

3 _ _ _ _ _

2 _ _ _ _ _

1 _ _ _ _

p a c k

Name _____

Lunchtime

Read the clues, then write the words.
Start at the bottom and climb to the top.

To flip over.
Change one letter.

— — — —

6

To be on fire.
Add a letter before the last letter.

— — — — —

5

You put a hot dog in a ___.
Take away two letters.

— — —

4

A group of things, like a ___ of grapes.
Take away one letter.

— — — — —

3

A combination of breakfast and lunch.
Take away one letter. Add two letters to the beginning.

— — — — — —

2

To hit with your fist.
Change one letter.

— — — — —

1

l u n c h

Daily Word Ladders for Fluency ■SCHOLASTIC

Name _____

Looking sharp

Read the clues, then write the words.
Start at the bottom and climb to the top.

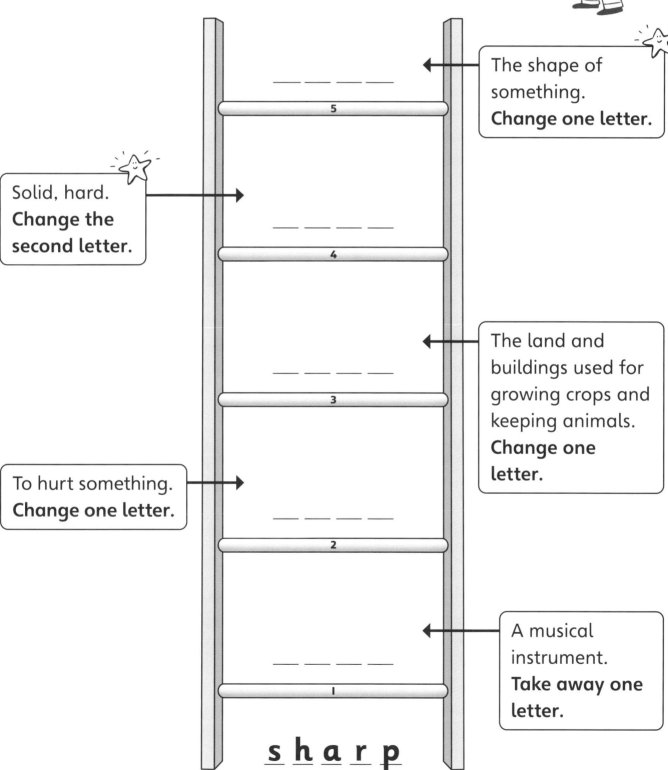

The shape of something. **Change one letter.**

5 _ _ _ _ _

Solid, hard. **Change the second letter.**

4 _ _ _ _

The land and buildings used for growing crops and keeping animals. **Change one letter.**

3 _ _ _ _

To hurt something. **Change one letter.**

2 _ _ _ _

A musical instrument. **Take away one letter.**

1 _ _ _ _

s h a r p

Name _____

Aww!

Read the clues, then write the words.
Start at the bottom and climb to the top.

A legal rule.
Change one letter.

→ ___ ___ ___

5

What a crow says.
Change one letter.

←

___ ___ ___

4

You cut wood with
a ___.
Change one letter.

→ ___ ___ ___

3

Not cooked.
Change one letter.

←

___ ___ ___

2

This moves
your mouth.
**Change the
first letter.**

→ ___ ___ ___

1

<u>p</u> <u>a</u> <u>w</u>

Name _____

Eww!

Read the clues, then write the words.
Start at the bottom and climb to the top.

5 — — — —
← Opposite of many. **Take away one letter.**

'The birds ___ across the sky.' **Change one letter.** →
4 — — — — —

3 — — — — —
← 'I ___ bubbles outside.' **Change the first two letters.**

'I ___ two inches last year.' **Take away the first letter. Add two letters to the beginning.** →
2 — — — — —

1 — — — —
← Not old. **Change one letter.**

<u>d</u> <u>e</u> <u>w</u>

Name _____

Look what you know

Read the clues, then write the words.
Start at the bottom and climb to the top.

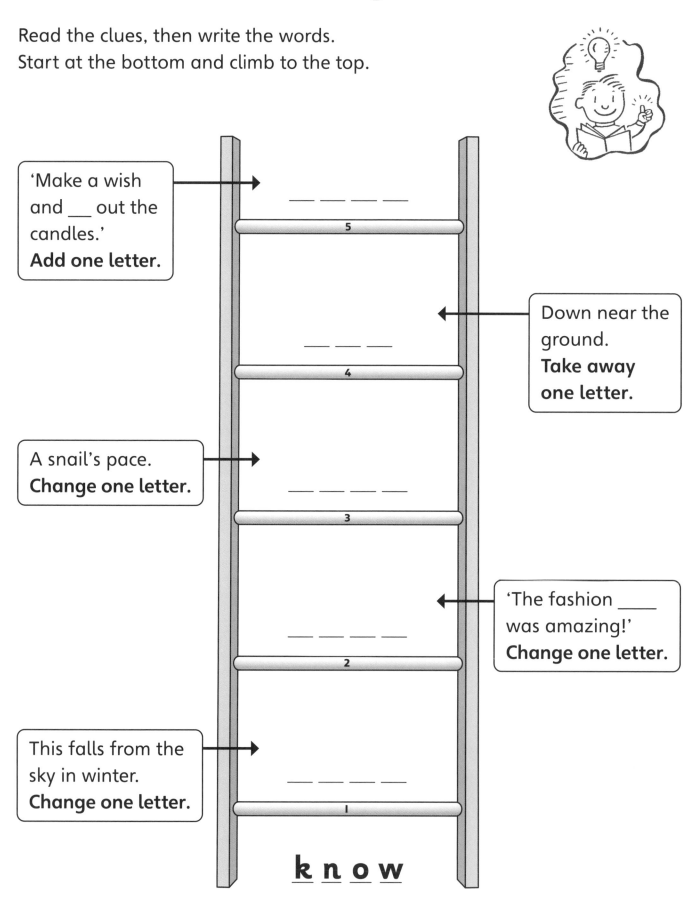

'Make a wish and ___ out the candles.'
Add one letter.

5 _ _ _ _ _

Down near the ground.
Take away one letter.

4 _ _ _

A snail's pace.
Change one letter.

3 _ _ _ _ _

'The fashion ____ was amazing!'
Change one letter.

2 _ _ _ _ _

This falls from the sky in winter.
Change one letter.

1 _ _ _ _

<u>k</u> <u>n</u> <u>o</u> <u>w</u>

Daily Word Ladders for Fluency **SCHOLASTIC**

Name _____

Moo, cow, moo

Read the clues, then write the words.
Start at the bottom and climb to the top.

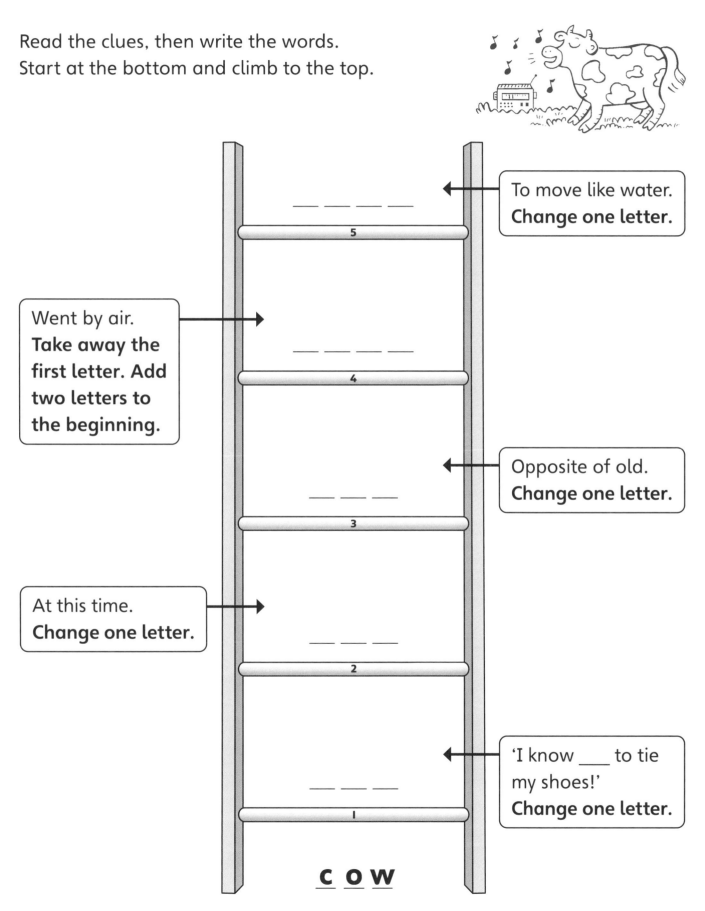

__ __ __ __
5

To move like water.
Change one letter.

__ __ __ __
4

Went by air.
Take away the first letter. Add two letters to the beginning.

__ __ __
3

Opposite of old.
Change one letter.

__ __ __
2

At this time.
Change one letter.

__ __ __
1

'I know ___ to tie my shoes!'
Change one letter.

<u>c</u> <u>o</u> <u>w</u>

Dig in the soil

Name _____

Read the clues, then write the words.
Start at the bottom and climb to the top.

A penny is a ___.
Change one letter.

___ ___ ___ ___

6

To put two or more things together.
Take away the last letter. Add two letters to the end.

___ ___ ___ ___

5

Happiness.
Change one letter.

___ ___ ___

4

Something to play with.
Change one letter.

___ ___ ___

3

Not a girl.
Take away the last two letters. Add one letter to the end.

___ ___ ___ ___

2

Really hot water will do this.
Change one letter.

___ ___ ___ ___

1

<u>s</u> <u>o</u> <u>i</u> <u>l</u>

Name _____

Ring, ring

Read the clues, then write the words.
Start at the bottom and climb to the top.

He wears a crown.
Change one letter.

5 _ _ _ _

'The bird had a broken ___.'
Take away one letter.

4 _ _ _ _

You move backwards and forwards on this at the playground.
Change one letter.

3 _ _ _ _ _

Bees might do this when they're angry.
Add one letter.

2 _ _ _ _

'I like to ___ songs.'
Change one letter.

1 _ _ _ _

r i n g

Name _____

Sing along

Read the clues, then write the words.
Start at the bottom and climb to the top.

'Yesterday we ___ *Happy Birthday* to Leila.'
Change one letter.

— — — —
6

'Please ___ your coat on the peg.'
Change one letter.

— — — —
5

A loud, popping noise.
Change one letter.

— — — —
4

'Her mobile phone ____ as she was getting off the train.'
Change one letter.

— — — —
3

Something you wear on your finger.
Take away two letters. Add one letter to the beginning.

— — — —
2

What a wasp might do to you.
Add one letter.

— — — — —
1

s i n g

Daily Word Ladders for Fluency **SCHOLASTIC**

Bring it on!

Read the clues, then write the words.
Start at the bottom and climb to the top.

6. _ _ _ _ _
→ You use this body part to breathe. **Change the second letter.**

Not short. Change one letter. →
5. _ _ _ _ _

4. _ _ _ _ _
← Something you sing. **Take away two letters.**

Opposite of weak. Change one letter. →
3. _ _ _ _ _ _

2. _ _ _ _ _ _
← You tie this to a kite. **Add two letters.**

'I did not hear the bell ___.' **Take away one letter.** →
1. _ _ _ _ _

b r i n g

Name _____

Power up

Read the clues, then write the words.
Start at the bottom and climb to the top.

To cut up something into small pieces. **Change one letter.** → _ _ _ _ _ 5

A place where you buy things. **Change one letter.** ← _ _ _ _ _ 4

'Will you ___ us how to play this game?' **Take away two letters.** → _ _ _ _ 3

Light rain. **Take away the first letter. Add two letters to the beginning.** ← _ _ _ _ _ _ _ 2

A tall building. **Change one letter.** → _ _ _ _ _ 1

p o w e r

Photocopiable

Daily Word Ladders for Fluency **≡SCHOLASTIC**

Name _____

Shadow puppets

Read the clues, then write the words.
Start at the bottom and climb to the top.

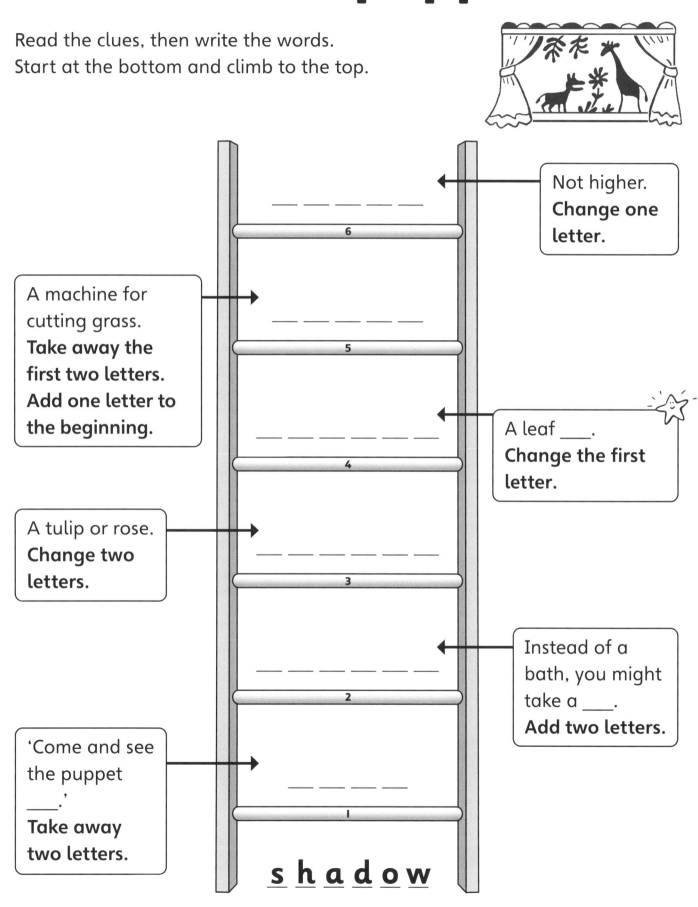

Not higher.
Change one letter.

A machine for cutting grass.
Take away the first two letters. Add one letter to the beginning.

A leaf ___.
Change the first letter.

A tulip or rose.
Change two letters.

Instead of a bath, you might take a ___.
Add two letters.

'Come and see the puppet ___.'
Take away two letters.

6

5

4

3

2

1

s h a d o w

SCHOLASTIC Daily Word Ladders for Fluency

Photocopiable

79

Colour change

Read the clues, then write the words.
Start at the bottom and climb to the top.

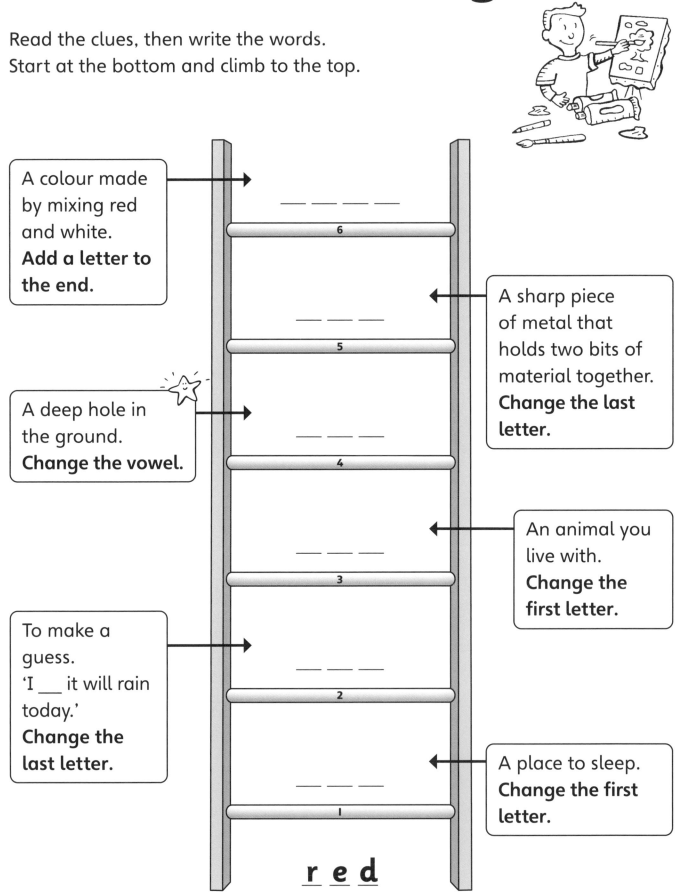

A colour made by mixing red and white. **Add a letter to the end.**

6 ___ ___ ___ ___

A sharp piece of metal that holds two bits of material together. **Change the last letter.**

5 ___ ___ ___

A deep hole in the ground. **Change the vowel.**

4 ___ ___ ___

An animal you live with. **Change the first letter.**

3 ___ ___ ___

To make a guess. 'I ___ it will rain today.' **Change the last letter.**

2 ___ ___ ___

A place to sleep. **Change the first letter.**

1 ___ ___ ___

r e d

Daily Word Ladders for Fluency **SCHOLASTIC**

A matter of size

Read the clues, then write the words.
Start at the bottom and climb to the top.

_ _ _ _ _

5

**Opposite of big.
Take away the
first letter, then
add two.**

**Opposite of short.
Change the first
letter.**

_ _ _ _

4

_ _ _ _

3

**A round object
used for playing
football.
Change the
vowel.**

**'Please could we
have the ___ for
our food?'
Take away the
last letter, then
add two.**

_ _ _ _

2

_ _ _

1

**A small amount.
Change the last
letter.**

<u>b</u> <u>i</u> <u>g</u>

Name _____

Sweet sounds

Read the clues, then write the words.
Start at the bottom and climb to the top.

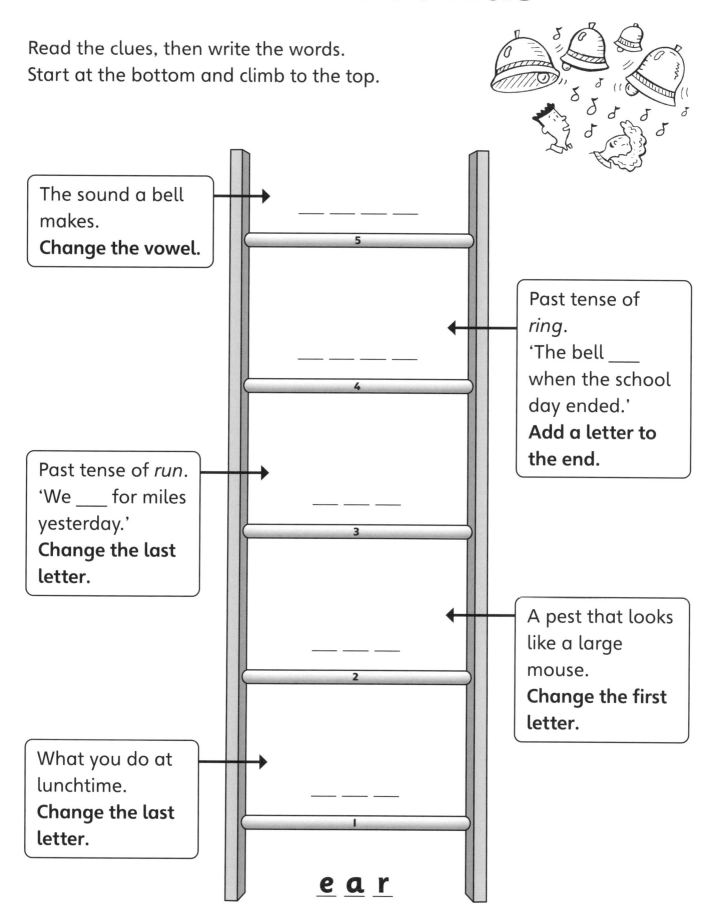

The sound a bell makes.
Change the vowel.

→ _ _ _ _ _

5

Past tense of *ring*.
'The bell ___ when the school day ended.'
Add a letter to the end.

_ _ _ _ ←

4

Past tense of *run*.
'We ___ for miles yesterday.'
Change the last letter.

→ _ _ _

3

A pest that looks like a large mouse.
Change the first letter.

_ _ _ ←

2

What you do at lunchtime.
Change the last letter.

→ _ _ _

1

<u>e</u> <u>a</u> <u>r</u>

Photocopiable

Daily Word Ladders for Fluency ■SCHOLASTIC

Name _____

Hop to it

Read the clues, then write the words.
Start at the bottom and climb to the top.

This looks like a frog with rough, bumpy skin.
Add a vowel after the first letter.

A tiny bit. 'The soup was a ___ cold.'
Change the last letter.

A piece of card or cloth that shows the price of something.
Change the vowel.

To pull at something. 'I felt a ___ on my sleeve.'
Change the first letter.

This holds liquid. 'Joe poured milk from the ___.'
Change the vowel.

A slow, steady run. 'Ayesha likes to ___ in the park.'
Take away the first two letters, then add one.

6 ＿ ＿ ＿ ＿

5 ＿ ＿ ＿

4 ＿ ＿ ＿

3 ＿ ＿ ＿

2 ＿ ＿ ＿

1 ＿ ＿ ＿

f r o g

Name _____

Warm and cosy

Read the clues, then write the words.
Start at the bottom and climb to the top.

This burns wood. **Change the first letter.**

_ _ _ _

5

A metal thread used to connect things to power. **Change the first vowel.**

_ _ _ _

4

Past tense of *wear*.
'Rory ___ new shoes yesterday.' **Change the first letter.**

_ _ _ _

3

To act in a dull way.
'The man on the TV is a ___.' **Change the last letter.**

_ _ _ _

2

Your birthday falls on the day you were ___. **Change the vowel.**

_ _ _ _

1

<u>b</u> <u>u</u> <u>r</u> <u>n</u>

Name _____

Glasses

Read the clues, then write the words.
Start at the bottom and climb to the top.

You use this to smell things. Change the first letter.

6 ___ ___ ___ ___

You do this when you have your school photo taken. 'Everyone smile and ___ for the picture.' Change the last letter.

5 ___ ___ ___ ___

A pole that helps hold up a fence. Change the vowel.

4 ___ ___ ___ ___

A long time ago. Add a letter before the last letter.

3 ___ ___ ___ ___

To touch gently. 'The coach gave me a ___ on the back.' Change the first letter.

2 ___ ___ ___

What you do at breakfast. Change the last letter.

1 ___ ___ ___

e a r

Top to bottom

Read the clues, then write the words.
Start at the bottom and climb to the top.

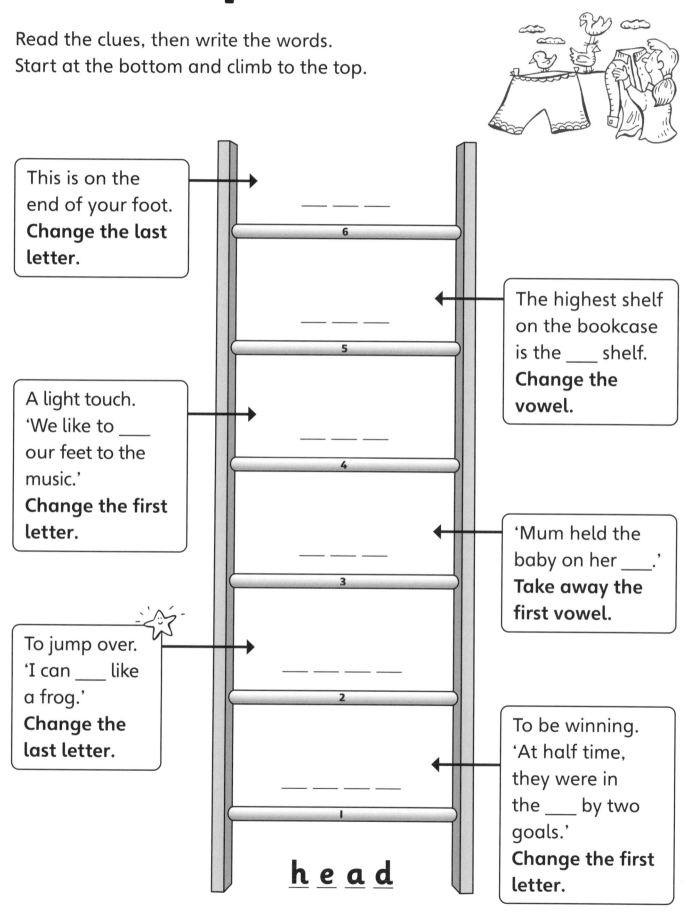

This is on the end of your foot. **Change the last letter.**

The highest shelf on the bookcase is the ___ shelf. **Change the vowel.**

A light touch. 'We like to ___ our feet to the music.' **Change the first letter.**

'Mum held the baby on her ___.' **Take away the first vowel.**

To jump over. 'I can ___ like a frog.' **Change the last letter.**

To be winning. 'At half time, they were in the ___ by two goals.' **Change the first letter.**

6
5
4
3
2
1

h e a d

Name _____

Different ways to travel

Read the clues, then write the words.
Start at the bottom and climb to the top.

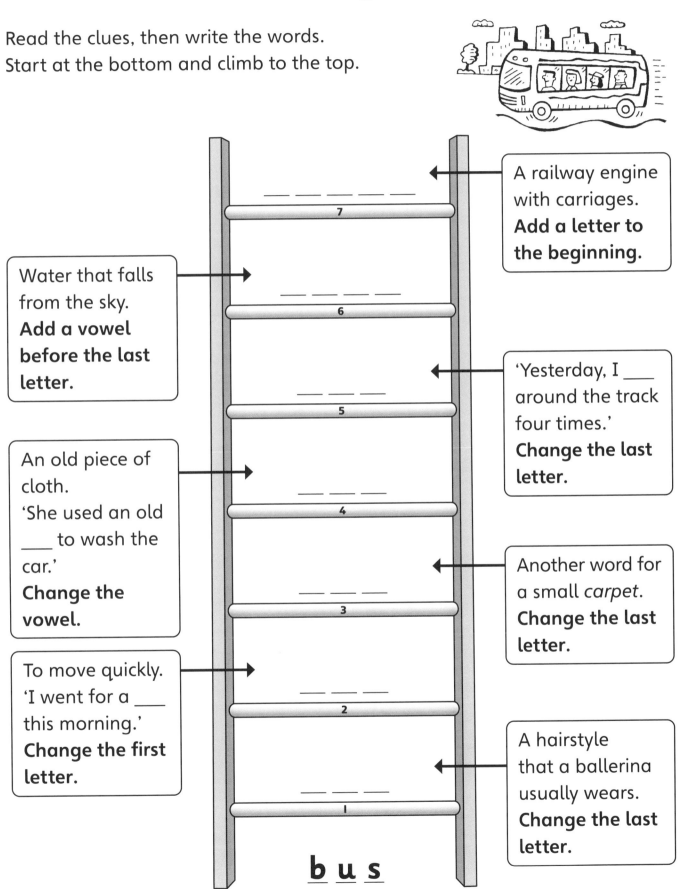

A railway engine with carriages. **Add a letter to the beginning.**

Water that falls from the sky. **Add a vowel before the last letter.**

'Yesterday, I ___ around the track four times.' **Change the last letter.**

An old piece of cloth. 'She used an old ___ to wash the car.' **Change the vowel.**

Another word for a small *carpet*. **Change the last letter.**

To move quickly. 'I went for a ___ this morning.' **Change the first letter.**

A hairstyle that a ballerina usually wears. **Change the last letter.**

7

6

5

4

3

2

1

b u s

Name _____

Fab fruits

Read the clues, then write the words.
Start at the bottom and climb to the top.

A sweet fruit that has furry skin. **Change the last letter.**

— — — — — —

5

Opposite of *war*. **Take away the last letter, then add two.**

— — — — — —

4

A green fruit that is shaped like a light bulb. **Add a letter to the end.**

— — — — —

3

This little round, green vegetable grows in a pod. **Rearrange the letters.**

— — —

2

Another word for *monkey*. **Take away the two letters before the last letter.**

— — — —

1

a p p l e

Daily Word Ladders for Fluency **SCHOLASTIC**

Name _____

Beautiful forests

Read the clues, then write the words.
Start at the bottom and climb to the top.

The colour of the sky. **Change the first letter.**

This is used to stick things together. **Take away the first letter, then add two.**

A short name for *Susan*. **Change the last letter.**

This lights up the day. **Take away the two vowels, then add one.**

'Have you ____ my coat?' **Change the first letter.**

A short word for *teenager*. **Take away the first two letters, then add one.**

6 — — — — —

5 — — — — —

4 — — — —

3 — — — —

2 — — — — —

1 — — — — —

g r e e n

Name _____

Deep sea divers

Read the clues, then write the words.
Start at the bottom and climb to the top.

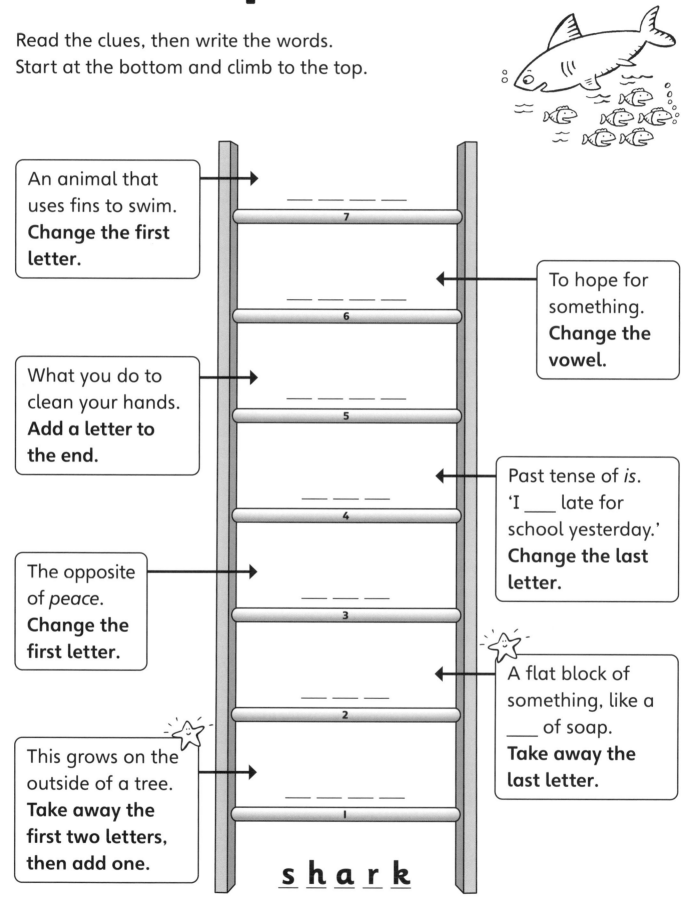

An animal that uses fins to swim. **Change the first letter.**

To hope for something. **Change the vowel.**

What you do to clean your hands. **Add a letter to the end.**

Past tense of *is*. 'I ___ late for school yesterday.' **Change the last letter.**

The opposite of *peace*. **Change the first letter.**

A flat block of something, like a ___ of soap. **Take away the last letter.**

This grows on the outside of a tree. **Take away the first two letters, then add one.**

s h a r k

Photocopiable

Daily Word Ladders for Fluency **SCHOLASTIC**

Toy shop

Read the clues, then write the words.
Start at the bottom and climb to the top.

_ _ _ _ _   **7**

A toy that looks like a baby. **Change the vowel.**

Not shiny. **Change the first letter.**

_ _ _ _ _   **6**

_ _ _ _ _   **5**

Filled to the top. **Change the first letter.**

A male cow. **Take away the last letter, then add two.**

_ _ _ _   **4**

_ _ _ _   **3**

A joining word. 'I want to come over, ____ I have to do my homework first.' **Change the last letter.**

To pay for something at a shop. **Change the vowel.**

_ _ _ _   **2**

_ _ _ _   **1**

Opposite of *girl*. **Change the first letter.**

t o y

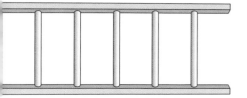
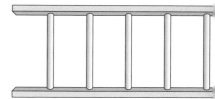

Answers

The first word for each page is the bottom of the ladder, the last word is the top of the ladder.

Run, cat, run! (page 8)
cat, sat, mat, bat

Pan-tastic (page 9)
pan, can, fan, man

Rats (page 10)
rat, rag, rap, ran

A pat on the back (page 11)
pat, pal, pan, pad

Jam with Sam (page 12)
jam, ham, Sam, sad, sat

Wag the tail (page 13)
wag, bag, tag, nag, nap

Everybody clap your hands (page 14)
clap, lap, tap, cap, cab, can

Camping (page 15)
camp, cap, cat, rat, mat, map

Jet set (page 16)
jet, wet, let, get

Bedtime (page 17)
bed, red, led, wed

Word web (page 18)
web, wet, net, pet

On the set (page 19)
set, wet, met, men, den

Make a dent (page 20)
dent, went, west, test, tent

Desk work (page 21)
desk, deck, neck, net, bet, bent

Ring the bell (page 22)
bell, tell, sell, fell, felt, melt

A big win (page 23)
win, pin, fin, tin

Put a lid on it (page 24)
lid, hid, rid, did

Pig fun (page 25)
pig, big, bit, bin, win

Sit down (page 26)
sit, spit, spin, shin, ship

Skipping (page 27)
skip, skin, shin, chin, chip, ship

Kiss, kiss (page 28)
kiss, miss, mist, fist, list, lift

Hot, hot, hot (page 29)
hot, pot, not, rot

Sad story (page 30)
sob, cob, job, rob

It's a job (page 31)
job, jog, jot, dot

Dogs (page 32)
dog, hog, hot, pot

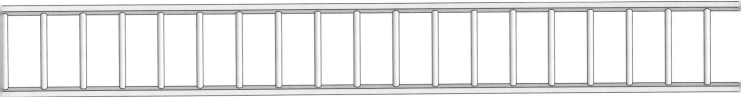

Mopping up (page 33)
mop, top, hop, hog, jog

Stop that! (page 34)
stop, shop, hop, hot, cot

Chop, chop! (page 35)
chop, shop, shot, hot, lot, lock

Socks (page 36)
sock, rock, rocket, locket, lock, clock

Fun in the sun (page 37)
fun, sun, run, bun

Good luck! (page 38)
luck, duck, tuck, stuck

Don't bug me (page 39)
bug, bus, bun, bud

Rub-a-dub-dub (page 40)
rub, rug, run, rung

Catch that bus (page 41)
bus, but, cut, cub, tub

Pump it up (page 42)
pump, lump, plump, bump, hump

Silly squirrel (page 43)
nut, cut, but, hut, hum, gum

Cluck, cluck (page 44)
cluck, luck, duck, yuck, tuck, truck

Make your bed (page 45)
bed, bad, sad, sand, send

Number one dad (page 46)
dad, did, hid, had, bad, bat

Get a leg up (page 47)
leg, peg, pig, pit, pot, pet

Bug on a log (page 48)
bug, big, dig, dog, hog, hug

Bat attack (page 49)
bat, but, cut, cot, cat, cap, cup

Tug of war (page 50)
tug, rug, rub, rob, job, jot, jet

Top hat (page 51)
hat, pat, pet, pit, pot, hot, hut

Tap dance (page 52)
tap, tape, cape, cane, mane, man

Top dog (page 53)
top, hop, hope, rope, mope, mop

Cup of tea (page 54)
cup, cop, mop, mope, mole, mule

High tide (page 55)
tide, ride, rude, rule, mule, mute, cute

Give a dog a bone (page 56)
bone, cone, cane, mane, make, lake, late

Swimming (page 57)
swim, skim, slim, slam, clam, clamp

Shipshape (page 58)
ship, shop, shot, shut, hut, hat

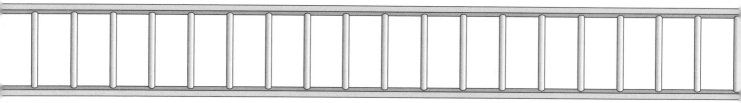

In a rush (page 59)
rush, rash, sash, mash, mush, much

Make a list (page 60)
list, lost, cost, cast, cash, wash, dash

Stack of books (page 61)
stack, snack, snap, snip, ship, shop, chop

Stamp it (page 62)
stamp, stack, tack, talk, chalk, walk, wall

Wishing well (page 63)
well, swell, smell, small, tall, talk, walk

Cow fun (page 64)
milk, mild, wild, will, wall, walk

Sort it out (page 65)
sort, sport, short, shore, score, core

Girl power (page 66)
girl, gill, hill, hall, ball, tall, tale

Pack your bags (page 67)
pack, park, spark, shark, dark, bark

Lunchtime (page 68)
lunch, punch, brunch, bunch, bun, burn, turn

Looking sharp (page 69)
sharp, harp, harm, farm, firm, form

Aww! (page 70)
paw, jaw, raw, saw, caw, law

Eww! (page 71)
dew, new, grew, blew, flew, few

Look what you know (page 72)
know, snow, show, slow, low, blow

Moo, cow, moo (page 73)
cow, how, now, new, flew, flow

Dig in the soil (page 74)
soil, boil, boy, toy, joy, join, coin

Ring, ring (page 75)
ring, sing, sting, swing, wing, king

Sing along (page 76)
sing, sting, ring, rang, bang, hang, sang

Bring it on! (page 77)
bring, ring, string, strong, song, long, lung

Power up (page 78)
power, tower, shower, show, shop, chop

Shadow puppets (page 79)
shadow, show, shower, flower, blower, mower, lower

Colour change (page 80)
red, bed, bet, pet, pit, pin, pink

A matter of size (page 81)
big, bit, bill, ball, tall, small

Sweet sounds (page 82)
ear, eat, rat, ran, rang, ring

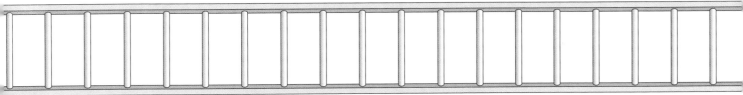

Hop to it (page 83)
frog, jog, jug, tug, tag, tad, toad

Warm and cosy (page 84)
burn, born, bore, wore, wire, fire

Glasses (page 85)
ear, eat, pat, past, post, pose, nose

Top to bottom (page 86)
head, lead, leap, lap, tap, top, toe

Different ways to travel (page 87)
bus, bun, run, rug, rag, ran, rain, train

Fab fruits (page 88)
apple, ape, pea, pear, peace, peach

Beautiful forests (page 89)
green, teen, seen, sun, Sue, glue, blue

Deep sea divers (page 90)
shark, bark, bar, war, was, wash, wish, fish

Toy shop (page 91)
toy, boy, buy, but, bull, full, dull, doll